980.3
NOR

Norman, James   5519

The riddle of
the Incas

DATE			
OCT 3 1			
NOV 2 2			
NOV 12			
NOV 25 84			
FAC			
SHIRLEY			
FAC 94-5			
FAC. 97/98			
OC 20 '00			

5519

The Riddle
of
The Incas

The Riddle of The Incas

The Story
of Hiram Bingham
and
Machu Picchu

by
**JAMES
NORMAN**

Illustrated by JIM FOX

Hawthorn Books, Inc. Publishers New York

THE RIDDLE OF THE INCAS: The Story of Hiram Bingham
and Machu Picchu

First Edition: 1968

Designed by Gene Gordon

2555

CONTENTS

5

The Riddle
of
The Incas

1.

SOMETHING HIDDEN

A *distant roar brought the small party of amateur ex-*plorers to a halt.

"What in the world is that?" asked one of the horsemen. "It sounds like a tremendous waterfall."

Hiram Bingham, the leader of the party, listened carefully. "That must be the river," he said, "but I didn't realize there would be a waterfall here."

A third man in the party, a young lieutenant of the Peruvian army, nodded enthusiastically. "It is not a waterfall," he said. "It is simply the Apurimac River rushing through its canyon. In the Indian tongue, Quichua, *Apurimac* means the Great Speaker. Its voice can be heard for miles."

The men listened for a moment to the impressive roar rising seven thousand feet from the floor of the canyon below them. Lieutenant Caceres glanced at the mid-February sun that showed faintly in the overcast sky and then said, "Perhaps we ought to camp here. The trail into the canyon is worse than what we have already covered. It will be dark in another hour. Do we camp, gentlemen?" He looked at Hiram Bingham, adding, "Should we stop, Señor Bingham?"

Bingham's glance went toward the other men of the party. Again it struck him. What a strange group this was to be traveling together in the wilds of Peru! What a mixture of nationalities! He himself had been born in Hawaii. His traveling companion, Clarence Hay, had been born in the United States. Lieutenant Caceres represented an elite Spanish family that had settled in Peru. The lieutenant's aide, a stocky soldier named Castillo, was an Indian. Another of the party was a young Peruvian rancher from Abancay; his companion was a Peruvian intellectual who wrote for a newspaper in Lima. Hiram had already dubbed the latter *El Periodista*. The remainder of the expedition was made up of pack bearers and mule skinners, all Quichua Indians.

Although the group had been together for only a day, Bingham could already measure each man's capabilities. He knew that Clarence Hay was tired, but was prepared to push on. El Periodista looked fairly fresh, yet he was always ready to quit. The lieutenant and his tireless, daredevil aide both looked as lively as they had at the

10

beginning of the day. Hiram did not even bother about the Quichua pack bearers. They were capable of going on for endless hours.

"I feel wo ohould push on," Bingham told Lieutenant Caceres. "We ought to reach the river as soon as possible. We want to be fresh when we make the crossing tomorrow and climb to Choqquequirau."

"Ah, yes—Choqquequirau," said the lieutenant. "Yes, Choqquequirau. We must get there by all means. We shall find the treasure, yes."

Hiram smiled. Although the small exploration party had been made up so that he and Clarence L. Hay, both Yale University men, could investigate the Inca ruins at Choqquequirau, the lieutenant, who had been assigned to guide them, was convinced it was a treasure hunt. Like almost everyone in Peru at this time—the year was 1909—the lieutenant, his aide, the rancher, and El Periodista felt that the only reason for visiting the countless ruins of the great pre-Hispanic civilizations was to dig for treasures. But Hiram and Clarence Hay had other reasons. The ruins at Choqquequirau especially fascinated them because the place was believed to be the secret retreat to which the last Inca emperors retired after the Spanish conquerors overthrew their empire. Hiram was intrigued by this, and also because Choqquequirau had been seen only three times by explorers during the past three hundred years.

"We march," Lieutenant Caceres shouted. The soldier, Castillo, reined his horse, urging it down the canyon trail. The party strung out in single file behind him.

Before long the trail down became difficult. Darkness filled the great hollow of the canyon and a light rain soaked the travelers. At one point the remains of an avalanche partly obliterated the route. Sensing the dangerous footing, the horses and mules trembled in fright, forcing the riders to dismount and lead them across the loose earth and rocks which threatened to slide from beneath them at any moment.

Hiram heard Lieutenant Caceres shouting, *"Valor, hombres.* Be intrepid, my friends."

What a marvelous man, Hiram thought. Even at the end of a hard day, and in this perilous darkness, the lieutenant's engaging enthusiasm never lets up. He's the perfect guide for an expedition.

El Periodista had begun to complain again. "We should go back," he protested. "We must wait for daylight. It is too dangerous."

"Valor, man," Caceres replied. "The danger is two weeks past. It was all of two weeks ago that some mules, crossing this place, set off the avalanche. They were swept down to the bottom of the canyon. You need not worry now."

The treacherous area was safely crossed. For an hour the party made satisfactory progress, finally reaching a small terrace that appeared to hang in the darkness above the river. The sound of the torrent below was so loud the men could hardly hear one another. Hiram saw El Periodista dismount; the journalist was ready to camp for the night.

"Not yet," Lieutenant Caceres shouted at the newspaperman. "We are still a thousand feet above the river. Be fearless, man. From here onward the rest is level ground."

In a journal that he kept, Hiram Bingham later noted

that the lieutenant's encouraging words, "The rest is level ground," turned out to be one of the lieutenant's little jokes. As Hiram followed the narrow path that was cut across the face of a precipice, he sensed that the going was dangerous. Later, when he saw it in daylight, he said, "We were insane to have tried it."

Hiram Bingham could feel the path drop steeply downward, in a series of vertical Zs. At one end of each sharp turn a ribbonlike waterfall dropped a sheer seven hundred feet; at the other end there was an equally sheer chasm. Here and there along the interminable descent, icy cataracts cut across the trail and had to be blindly leaped.

At last, Bingham saw a dim light ahead. It was a lantern being waved by Castillo to guide the explorers toward a small terrace near the river. The river could not be seen in the darkness, but the roar of the water was so loud no one's voice could be heard. Gesturing with his arms, Castillo pointed the way toward two small reed huts, the camp for the night.

The next morning Bingham and Hay, their muscles aching and their bones stiff from the previous day's hard ride, crawled from their tiny hut to get their first view of the raging river. Hiram was stunned by his first glimpse of it. Although the river was at least 250 feet wide, it slammed through the canyon at a wild pace, throwing up waves like a sea whipped by a gale. A long, slender bridge, supported by six strands of telegraph wire, spanned the wild torrent.

"Good Lord, are we going across that?" Hay shouted.

Hiram nodded. He was not as troubled by the sight of the fragile bridge as by the knowledge of how it had been built. The last exploring party to visit Choqque-quirau had been organized by the prefect of the district, J. J. Nuñez, and led by Lieutenant Caceres. These men had cut the trail down to the river. When their way had seemed impossibly blocked by the frightful rapids, a Chinese peddler named Don Mariano had come forward with a daring solution. He tied a stout string to his waist and, to everyone's amazement, he swam the river. He was then able to pull a heavier rope over, and then the cables.

As Bingham and Hay stared at the tormented water which flung icy spray as high as the suspension bridge, Lieutenant Caceres joined them. The lieutenant cupped his hands to Bingham's ear, shouting, "The rains have made the river quite high. It has risen more than fifty feet. The water is at least a hundred feet deep here."

"How high above us are the ruins?" Bingham shouted back.

Caceres pointed toward the opposite wall of the canyon. Cupping his hands, he shouted, "The river at this point is about five thousand feet above sea level; the ruins are six thousand feet higher. We must do it on foot because the pack animals cannot cross the bridge. There is not much of a trail, anyway."

After breakfast the members of the expedition crept, one at a time, on hands and knees across the swaying bridge. El Periodista, however, refused to go. He had decided it was wiser to remain at the river camp with the mule drivers and their animals. After all, he had to write up his notes for the newspaper in Lima. "Perhaps I'll follow later," he said.

Shortly after crossing the river, Hiram Bingham real-

14

ized how wise El Periodista was. The trail up the canyon wall was slippery and overgrown with dense brush. At times the angle was so steep he had to crawl on all fours. Now and then the path was cut by a waterfall or by streams bridged by single ice-smooth logs. Despite Lieutenant Caceres' ringing voice shouting, *"Valor, hombres,"* progress was snaillike: a climb of fifty feet in the rarefied air, a pause, another climb, another pause.

At last the highest point on the canyon trail was reached. Feeling that his lungs would burst if he went another foot, Hiram called for a brief stop. It was a marvelous pause. Far below him the white torrent of the Apurimac River raced through the canyon, its voice reaching up distantly. The great canyon valley was rimmed by mountains that appeared to be no larger than hills because beyond them there were endless ranges of towering snow-capped mountains.

"I'll bet," Hiram said to Hay, "that if you took the whole range of our White Mountains or our Great Smokies of Tennessee and North Carolina and put them at the floor of this valley, they wouldn't come more than halfway to the top."

Once again the party pressed on, following the trail westward, skirting more precipices, crossing more icy torrents until, around two o'clock, Lieutenant Caceres called out, "There, gentlemen, there it is—Choqque-quirau."

Now, carrying only their lightest packs, Bingham, Hay, the lieutenant, and the rancher hurried ahead, leaving the Quichua bearers to follow at a more leisurely pace. In the mountains, distances are deceptive. Hiram had expected to reach the ruins within a short time, but

15

it was four o'clock before they reached their goal. As Hiram scrambled up a last rocky promontory, he heard a cry of warning from Caceres. At the same instant an enormous shadow swept over him.

He crouched among the rocks and froze, staring at a huge condor wheeling in the air overhead. This king of Andean birds had a wingspread of at least twelve feet. As it circled, coming lower and lower, Hiram could clearly see its cruel beak and powerful talons. He knew that shepherds in the high Andean pastures waged a constant battle against condors. The birds were so powerful they could easily lift and carry off sheep. At the moment he felt helpless; he had neither gun nor club with which to ward off an attack.

Frantically groping for a stone that he might throw, his fingers picked up pebbles. They would be about as effective as peas against the huge bird. Then he saw Lieutenant Caceres unholstering his pistol. At the same moment, the condor sailed away in a great arc.

Hiram breathed a sigh of relief. "Why didn't you shoot it?" he asked Caceres. "That monster could have given me a bad tumble."

"I was prepared," replied the lieutenant. "However, we do not like to shoot them; they are so few, now. This one was curious, nothing more. Sometimes they are not at all friendly. When I was here with the prefect, and our men were clearing brush, the condors bothered us a great deal."

During the remaining hours of daylight, the explorers made a hasty survey of the ancient mountaintop stronghold which the condor seemed to think was his private domain. While Castillo made camp, constructing grass

16

huts, the others climbed through the ruins clustered in several groups on terraces and natural shelves reached by stone stairways and winding paths.

That evening, shivering in Castillo's grass huts because the pack bearers had not arrived with their blankets and camping gear, Hiram and Clarence Hay discussed what they should do during their stay on the mountain. The ruins were somewhat larger than they had anticipated.

"How can we be sure if this was the last Inca stronghold?" Hay asked. "How do we go about all this?"

Bingham gave an ironic chuckle. "I'm not sure myself," he said. "I really know very little about the Incas —only what I've read in Prescott. I'm not an archaeologist, you know."

"Well, we might search for buried treasures," Hay suggested. "That's what Caceres and the others expect us to do. Everyone says that when the Incas fled from Cuzco they took their golden treasures. Maybe the stuff is buried here."

"I'm dubious about Inca treasures," replied Hiram. "But I have a treasure of another kind. It's just what we need."

Holding a candle above his knapsack, he rummaged inside, digging out a small handbook. It was entitled *Hints to Travelers,* and was published by the British Royal Geographical Society. He paged through it rapidly. "Ah, here is exactly what we need," he murmured. "It's a chapter called *What Should Be Done When One Is Confronted by a Prehistoric Site.* It says, 'Take careful measurements and plenty of photographs. Describe as accurately as possible all finds.'"

During his four days on the mountain, Hiram Bingham followed the instructions in the guidebook. He and Hay measured the ruins of the most important buildings of Choqquequirau, and they made a rough map of the site. They snapped numerous photographs. Not all the pictures came out well because the weather was miserable; when it was not misting or raining, the mountaintop was shrouded in clouds.

The ruins covered three areas. The first area was at the edge of the canyon, overlooking the ribbonlike river far below. The second area, which included the largest and most important buildings, was located on a saddle ridge somewhat to the north of the first area. Although the construction of these dwellings was clearly Inca, the workmanship was crude compared to Inca ruins Hiram had visited in the ancient Peruvian capital, Cuzco. The third group of ruins, much less extensive, was situated on a high spur about fifty yards beyond the middle area.

Among the ruins of the middle group, Hiram found several slate slabs upon which previous visitors had scratched their names and the dates of their visits. The earliest traveler to leave his register was a French explorer, Eugène de Sartiges. He had been accompanied by two Peruvians, José María Tejada and Marcelino León. Their date was 1834. Another party of three—José Benigno Samanez, Juan Rivas Plata, and Mariano Cisneros—had made the difficult journey in 1861. A last group had been the party of Lieutenant Caceres and the prefect of the district. Hiram noted the various dates and names, intending to check later and see if these men had left any written reports of their travels.

Although Bingham and his friends spent several days digging shafts and test trenches, hoping to turn up Inca artifacts, nothing of great value was found. To Hiram this was most disappointing. He had hoped to find cooking utensils, weapons, and tools that would help identify the people who once occupied this place.

For a moment Hiram's hopes rose when the Indian diggers came upon some ancient graves containing skulls and bones. Although it would have been important to take some of these finds back to Yale, where laboratory specialists might have studied them, this proved impossible. The skulls and bones were so old they crumbled at the touch of a finger. All that Hiram could do was to measure them.

The Quichua Indians watched with interest as the graves were probed, but the moment Hiram began measuring the bones they became upset.

"You make them nervous," said Castillo, translating from Quichua. "They are frightened because they no longer believe you are digging for treasures. They say you have come here to commune with the spirits of the departed Incas. This is bad. They want to go home."

Hiram decided to leave the bones undisturbed. Actually, he had seen enough of Choqquequirau. He was quite sure that this place had not been the last home of the Inca emperors. When he discussed this with Clarence Hay, he elaborated his reasons.

"I'm convinced, just from the position of the ruins, that Choqquequirau was a frontier fortress, not the last home of the Inca leaders. This place is a perfect fortress. I suspect it was built here as an outpost guarding the

19

upper valley of the Apurimac. It served to protect the old Inca capital, Cuzco, from the barbaric Indians who often came up the valley from the Amazon region."

"Furthermore," Hiram explained, "there seem to be no signs that the last Incas held their royal court here. The graves we uncovered appear to have been undisturbed for centuries. Yet, in them, we found no artifacts of importance, nothing made of gold, silver or bronze. It seems to me that no Inca nobles lived here."

"Well, I wish we hadn't wasted our time coming here," Hay said. "I've been soaked, clammy, and cold for four days."

"It was no waste of time," Hiram replied cheerfully. "We've seen it. Anyway, El Periodista will enjoy our report."

Hay smiled, amused. "I wonder what he'll write for the Lima paper."

"You can be sure it will be more vivid than if he had come with us," said Hiram.

His prediction about El Periodista proved correct. Two weeks later, in Lima, he read the journalist's articles. They described daring adventures, avalanches, ruins, and treasures.

Although Hiram was disappointed with the ruins at Choqquequirau, his imagination was stirred. If Choqquequirau were not the last city of the Incas, he asked himself, where, then, had the Inca emperors established themselves for forty years after being driven from Cuzco by the Spaniards?

Before departing from the mountaintop stronghold, he stood on the Inca lookout point and stared northward. It was like being on the top of the world. He could see

20

green mountains piling one upon another, deep valleys lost in shadows, a majestic and mysterious panorama dominated by the snowy peaks of Mount Salcantay and Mount Soray soaring twenty thousand feet into the heavens. If Choqquequirau were not the last Inca refuge, perhaps the refuge lay somewhere in that maze of unexplored mountains and valleys.

His imagination was stirred by the spell of the beckoning distances, and by the famous lines from Rudyard Kipling's *The Explorer* which he had read as a boy:

"Something hidden! Go and find it! Go and look
    behind the ranges.
"Something lost behind the ranges. Lost and wait-
    ing for you.
"Go!"

2.

THE EDUCATION OF AN EXPLORER

When Hiram Bingham stood on the misty heights above the Apurimac River, he did not know that the taunting phrase—"Something hidden! Go and find it!"—would call him back to Peru on the strangest quest in his life. He would soon find his place in that notable gallery of amateur explorers who discovered lost cities. He would be another Heinrich Schliemann, the discoverer of Homer's Troy. He would follow in the footsteps of a fellow American, John L. Stevens, who put aside his law practice to hunt for and find magnificent, forgotten cities in the Central American jungles which no one, at the time, believed were there.

What made Hiram Bingham an explorer? His classmates at Yale hardly thought of him as a person who could be comfortable trekking through wild country, sleeping in flea-infested Indian huts, or sharing roasted guinea pigs with primitive men. At college he was a nimble-witted, pleasant young man. He was a member of university clubs and attended functions. Although he enjoyed outdoor life, hiking and climbing, his friends felt he was too practical and conservative to chase after will-o'-the-wisp lost cities. They expected him to become a parson or a missionary. There was a leaning toward such vocations in the Bingham family.

His grandfather, Hiram Bingham I, had set the pace. Grandfather Bingham had been a lean, courageous, hardheaded New Englander, a Calvinist minister who toiled among the romantic South Sea Islanders. He sailed to Samoa as a missionary, then settled in Hawaii where he preached his first sermon in 1820. After building the first Christian church on Oahu, he wrote the first Hawaiian-English dictionary. Hiram's father, bearing the same name, carried on as a missionary in Hawaii, enlarging his father's parish and translating the Bible into Hawaiian.

On November 19, 1875, Hiram Bingham was born in Hawaii. Although young Hiram received his early schooling and passed his boyhood on one of the most exotic islands in the world, his education smacked of distant New England. His father, a stern, yet kindly man, gave him a solid Calvinist upbringing. Early in life Hiram was taught certain lessons that may have turned

23

him toward exploring. His father taught him to respect people of other races, to respect their ways and customs, no matter how primitive they might appear. His father also instilled in him a sense of curiosity, an interest in searching for unknown facts, and a love for the out-of-doors.

In later years Hiram recalled, "My father taught me to love mountain climbing. He took me on my first steep climb when I was just four years old. Later we climbed a number of mountains in the suburbs of Honolulu."

Father and son accepted the challenge of scaling almost every Hawaiian peak; they enjoyed the reward of standing upon the crests and wondering what lay beyond the next range. They shared the startling beauty of the Nuuanu Pali near Honolulu, the enchanting view of the Koolau Ditch on Maui, and the thrill of climbing Mauna Kea, the highest peak in the Pacific.

Although three generations of Binghams lived in Hawaii, when it came time for college they turned to New England. Young Hiram enrolled at Yale University in New Haven, Connecticut. Although he was a good scholar, he was never a drudge. He was jovial and had a pleasant sense of humor, but he was also seriously interested in his faith, for he conducted a Bible class and organized a boys' missionary club. However, nothing about his undergraduate days made much of an impression on his classmates. In the graduating class prediction, no one thought he would greatly distinguish himself.

Receiving his Bachelor of Arts degree from Yale in 1898, Hiram returned to Hawaii. Both his mother and father wanted him to study for the ministry. For a short period he gave the missionary calling a try, serving as the superintendent of a mission chapel in Honolulu. Finally deciding that he was not cut out to be a clergyman, he returned to the United States and studied at the University of California where he received his Master of Arts degree in 1900. While in California he realized that there was almost no research being done in Latin American history. He decided to become one of the pioneer scholars specializing in this field. Now, having definitely chosen his career, he returned to Harvard as a graduate instructor, while at the same time studying for a master's degree and his Ph.D. in history, which he received in 1905.

During the next two years Hiram taught at Princeton University. Teaching, however, did not appeal to him as much as research. Since he was especially fascinated by that three-hundred-year period of Spanish domination in South America—the period between the conquest of those lands by Cortés and Pizarro in the early 1500s, and their breaking free from Spain in the early 1800s—he undertook a trip to South America. For several months in 1906, he traveled by horseback, by carriage, and on foot through Venezuela and Colombia, following the incredible route taken in 1819 by the South American liberator, Simón Bolívar. He traced the route of Bolívar's raggle-taggle army of British and Irish volunteers, and Venezuelan patriots, from the tropical plains and swamps, up over the freezing passes of the Andes, to where the rebels met and defeated a royalist army, thus breaking Spain's hold on South America.

After publishing his report of the remarkable journey, Hiram returned to Yale to occupy an exciting new post

25

as curator of South American history for the university's library. He helped build the library's Latin American collection into one of the finest in the United States.

It was, however, his report on Bolívar's expedition that turned him into an explorer. The paper had attracted a good deal of attention and eventually caught the eye of the noted lawyer and Republican Party leader, Elihu Root, who was Theodore Roosevelt's Secretary of State. Root, at this time, was deeply interested in Latin America. One day he called the young professor to his office.

"I read your report with keen interest," he told Bingham. "Would you be interested in seeing more of South America?"

Hiram was both puzzled and startled. "I would, sir," he replied, "but at the moment I have duties at the university."

"We'll see to that," said the Secretary. "Next December the first Pan-American Scientific Congress will be held in Santiago, Chile. I propose appointing you as the Yale University delegate and as representative of our government."

For a young man of thirty-one, who was just beginning to settle into a professional career, the opportunity was an exciting one. In those days such plums usually went to far older and more experienced men. Bingham felt tremendously honored. He was also delighted because Secretary Root and Yale gave him what amounted to a carte blanche as to the time he could spend and the ground he could cover south of the Equator. He decided to use his time well.

In addition to attending the Scientific Congress, he

planned another research project. Instead of sailing directly to Chile for the two weeks of meetings, he decided to set out early enough to follow the old Spanish trade route, the most historic highway in South America, which linked Buenos Aires to Potosí and Lima. It was a road that had been pioneered by the ancient Incas, used by their conqueror Pizarro, by Spanish viceroys, by silver mine owners and Spanish cavalry, by the patriot armies of Argentina, and by Bolívar and Sucre, who marched over it in their final campaigns of the Wars of Independence.

Traveling with a fellow Yale man, Huntington Smith, Jr., who would also attend the conference in Santiago, Bingham sailed from New York in September 1908. The travelers took what was then the shortest route to Brazil and Argentina: they went first to London, where scheduled steamers left weekly for South America. To pass the time while at sea, they brought along numerous books about South America. They were particularly intrigued by Sir Clement Markham's *Cuzco and Peru,* and by Lieutenant Gibbon's vivid *Explorations of the Valley of the Amazon.* Before the voyage was over, Hiram Bingham was dreaming of making a trip down the Amazon.

After visiting in Río de Janeiro, Bingham and Smith went to Buenos Aires, where on November 18, 1908, they set out to follow the route of the historic colonial highway. Reaching the town of La Quiaca, Argentina, on the border of Argentina and Bolivia, they received an unexpected greeting.

They had checked into a half-completed hotel around nine o'clock in the evening, when, a few minutes later,

27

there was an authoritative knock at the door. On opening the door Hiram saw two rough-looking, unshaven men; both were armed with pistols. One of the men asked in English, "Are you the new Americans?"

Before Bingham could reply, they pushed into the room and shut the door behind them. "Who the devil are you?" Hiram asked.

"We might be friends," said one of the men.

"Well, what can I do for you gentlemen?"

"Nothing," the same man replied. "We just wanted to talk. Never see many Americans in these parts. You and your friend with the mining companies?"

"No, we're not in mining," said Hiram. He then explained that he and Smith were from Yale University and were en route to Santiago for the Scientific Congress.

"Professors, eh?" The two tough-looking men exchanged glances.

"What do you want with us?" Smith asked.

"You carrying much money?" asked one of the men.

"Very little," said Hiram. "It's too dangerous. We carry letters of credit. If they are stolen, they do the thief no good. But why do you ask this?"

"You being Americans, we just wanted to warn you about bandits in these parts." The man went on to tell some harrowing tales about how thick the region was with highwaymen.

"American bandits?" Bingham asked.

"Yes, American bandits, too. There is one band of them who were driven out of the United States by Pinkerton's police. They're very bad men to deal with, but if you are just professors and do not bother them, they won't bother you."

Now, almost as abruptly as they had come, the two men cordially shook hands with Bingham and Smith, and then left the room. A few minutes later Hiram went to the patio of the inn and asked the owner if he had seen their two visitors.

"Yes, of course," replied the innkeeper.

"Who are they?"

"Well, Señor, they are bandits."

"Bandits! But what are they doing here?"

The innkeeper shrugged with Latin eloquence, replying, "*Pues*, Señor, they came to look at you and your companion. They wish to make sure you are not American police, perhaps hired by the mining companies. They are part of the band that makes a living robbing the mine company payrolls."

"But why aren't they arrested?"

"They rob on the other side of the border, in Bolivia. Were they friendly when they left, Señor?"

"Yes, I believe they were."

"Then you need have no worry, Señor. They will not trouble you on the road."

Despite the reassuring words of the innkeeper, when the travelers continued on their way by stagecoach into Bolivia, they expected to be robbed at every turn of the trail. Holding up the stage would have been an easy task for bandits; the route was so steep and rocky that the coach moved at a snail's pace. There was no soldier-escort, although the driver was armed. His assistant was a barefoot Indian boy who trotted beside the mules, pelting them with stones that he threw with unerring accuracy.

After several days the stage line came to an end; Bing-

29

ham and Smith continued on horseback, crossing the bleak, parched, mountainous countryside. The only other travelers they encountered were the drivers of llama pack trains. When Hiram first saw the llamas, his sense of humor was tickled. The llamas moved with a slow, haughty bearing; they stretched their long necks and peered around like near-sighted dowagers.

"They remind me of some very proper Bostonian who finds himself at the wrong social function," said Hiram. Then he quoted an appropriate doggerel:

He looked about him with that air
Of supercilious despair
That very stuck-up people wear
At some society affair
When no one of their set is there.

Finally reaching the great silver-mining city of Potosí, Bingham and Smith went by railroad to the Pacific coast port of Antofagasta, took a steamer south to Valparaiso, Chile, arriving in Santiago in time to attend the Pan-American Scientific Congress. There the two young men hobnobbed with South America's leading intellectuals. One of these men, the noted Peruvian historian Don Carlos Romero, was fascinated by the story of their journey along the colonial highway.

"You have seen much of South America, yet not enough," said Don Carlos. "You must now cap your trip with a visit to my country. Above all, you must see the Inca ruins near Lake Titicaca and at Cuzco."

"That would be a rather extended journey," replied

Bingham. "Our time is limited. Perhaps we'll come back."

"Ah, no. You must see Cuzco," Don Carlos insisted. "It is an easy journey. You simply sail from Valparaiso to Arica, then go by train to La Paz, to Cuzco, then by stage to Lima, and finally sail home."

Although Bingham felt he had had his fill of travel for the moment, and he knew that Smith had to go home immediately after the congress, he remembered Secretary Root's parting instructions. Root had told them that they were good-will ambassadors of their country; they must endeavor in every way to please the officials of the countries they visited.

Hiram Bingham finally agreed to go to Cuzco. Although Smith sailed for New York, Hiram found another traveling companion—Clarence Hay, a Yale classmate and close friend, who was traveling in South America. Hay agreed to meet him in Peru.

Although Cuzco, at that time, was one of the dirtiest cities in the Americas—its rough cobbled streets littered with rubbish, its open sewers smelling rankly—it fascinated Hiram Bingham. At every turn there were impressive Inca ruins to poke into and admire. Day after day, Bingham and Hay picked their way through the dirty streets to visit the remains of ancient palaces, the religious temples, and the houses of the Inca Chosen Women who were called the Virgins of the Sun.

The two men were most impressed by the amazing engineering skills of the ancient people. Although the Incas had developed no tools harder than bronze, although they had no powerful work animals and no

31

wheeled vehicles, they had been able to move gigantic rocks and stone lintels into place. They shaped and fitted the rocks together so perfectly that no cement was needed. On the heights overlooking the city, the Incas had left the fortress, Sacsahuaman, which Bingham felt was the most extraordinary structure built by ancient man in the Western Hemisphere. The fortress had an outer wall twelve hundred feet long, with an average height of twenty-seven feet. The smaller stone blocks making up the wall weighed ten to twenty tons; one of the larger blocks was thirty-eight feet long, eighteen feet high and six feet thick. These blocks were fitted together so perfectly that a knife blade could not be inserted between them.

By mid-February Hiram Bingham felt that he had seen and absorbed enough. His mind was crammed with unusual impressions. He had not only visited all the ruins in and around Cuzco, but he had spent countless evenings with antiquarians from the University of Cuzco, discussing the history and customs of the Incas.

"It's time to head home," he told Clarence Hay. "I haven't seen my family in six months."

Just as the two friends began preparing for their homeward trip, Hiram Bingham had a visitor. The man was Don José J. Nuñez, the chief official or prefect of the province of Apurimac. He had come all the way from his district especially to see the American scholars.

"I urge you to visit my province," he explained. "You must explore the ruins at Choqquequirau so that you can report their importance to the President of Peru."

"We're going home," said Hiram.

"But this is most important," said the prefect. "I will

provide you with horses, bearers, and a military escort."

"Sir, this is no time to visit ruins," Hiram objected, as politely as he could. "We're in the height of the rainy season. People here tell us it is the rainiest month of the rainiest season in a quarter of a century. I should like to visit Choqquequirau, but at some better time."

"But, Señor, a report must be made for the President."

"This may be true, but I'm not an archaeologist," said Hiram.

The prefect stared at him unbelievingly. "You were a delegate at the Scientific Congress, yes?"

"Yes, I represented my government."

"And you are a doctor, Señor?"

"Yes, I have my Ph.D."

"Well then, you must know all about archaeology. You must know where to look for buried treasures."

"I'm sorry, Señor Nuñez, I am simply a history professor."

"Ah, you are modest, *señor profesor*. Now you will be my guest. You will visit Choqquequirau."

Hiram looked desperately to his companion for help. "What do we do, Clarence?"

Clarence Hay seemed more amused than disturbed. He shrugged, saying, "What can you do? Remember the instructions Secretary Root gave before you left New York."

Hiram gave a tired sigh. "Well, I guess it's Choqquequirau, then," he said.

Although the Inca ruins hanging above the Apurimac River were the last place he wanted to visit that wet February, years later he admitted that this was an important turning point in his life.

"Had it not been for Prefect Nuñez and his very practical interest in Choqquequirau, I should probably never have been tempted to look for Inca ruins and thus find two cities which had been lost to geographical knowledge for several centuries."

3.

THE INCA EMPIRE

In 1909, when Hiram Bingham and Clarence Hay vis-
ited Choqquequirau, very little was known about the
ancient Andean world where primitive men had hunted
and collected seeds as early as ten thousand years before. Little or nothing was known concerning the period
when those men showed signs of civilized activity, beginning to plant crops and build ceremonial cities.

Although Europeans and Americans had become extremely interested in the study of antiquities during the
latter half of the nineteenth century, their methods and

tools of research were scarcely scientific. Adventurous young men scrambled through the ruins of Greece, Egypt, and Rome. Even more daring men plunged into the jungles of Central America and Mexico, gradually piecing together the jigsaw puzzle of the ancient cultures in those regions. But archaeology at the turn of the century was still in its infancy. It was more pragmatic and descriptive than it was scientific and imaginative. The antiquarians of that era simply measured, catalogued, and described the things they found; afterward, with the help of historians, they made educated guesses concerning the past civilizations they studied.

When Hiram Bingham became interested in Peru, almost nothing was known about the region's ancient past. Hiram was aware that man's presence there was quite old, because, in 1835, the Danish naturalist T. W. Lund had explored some eight hundred caves in the Lagoa Santa district of Brazil, where he found the bones of extinct prehistoric animals—primitive horses and mastodons—along with human bones. This meant that early men were hunting in the vast region stretching from Ecuador and Peru down to Argentina sometime between twelve thousand and seven thousand years before.

At some distant time in the past, the hunters began collecting seeds, planting and harvesting, and domesticating animals. In time they began living in civilized communities. They developed crops that were unknown to Europe before the fifteenth century: corn, several varieties of beans, the white potato, sweet potatoes, peanuts, the chocolate bean, pineapples, cocoa, tobacco, avocados, and *quinoa* (a species of edible pig weed).

For meat some of these early people ate a dozen different kinds of *cuy*, rodents which we call guinea pigs.

Their most important domesticated animals, however, were the guanaco, and the related vicuña. Both of these animals are cousins of the camel. The Peruvians developed them into several breeds: the llama, for service as a beast of burden; the alpaca, which provided a heavy wool for weaving; and finally, the vicuña, which remained wild and was the source of the finest wool. Although the llama, because of its slender form, could not carry loads heavier than one hundred pounds, it was still a very useful animal. Unlike the European horse or ox, it required practically no care. Large flocks of llama could be grazed for months at a time on the high Andean pasture lands.

Although scholars in Hiram Bingham's time knew that the story of civilized man in Peru must reach back countless centuries, no one knew how far back it actually went. The only part of the story about which they really had any detailed information was the last stage, the period of Inca supremacy. And even the facts about the Incas were muddled. Whereas other great civilizations—the Egyptian or Greek—left written records for man to study, the Incas had no written language of any kind. What was known about their history and customs was recorded by the Spaniards who conquered them in the sixteenth century.

From such documents, and from the ruins he visited, Hiram Bingham knew that the Incas had reached a high level of civilization and had created the greatest empire in the Americas. These Peruvians were skilled craftsmen in many fields of endeavor. They wove their native cotton and vicuña wool into fine fabrics; they made garments which were colorfully adorned with horizontal or diagonal designs, brocaded with figures of birds, animals, and fish. In a museum he visited, Hiram saw a segment of their tapestry weaving that had five hundred two-ply wool wefts per inch—a most remarkable achievement when compared to the best tapestry weaving of Medieval Europe, which seldom had more than a hundred wefts to the inch.

Although the Incas had no potter's wheel, they made handsome pottery vessels as well as dishes decorated with graceful designs. In the working of metals, too, their artisans were highly skilled. Though they had no knowledge of iron, they shaped and cast copper and bronze, as well as gold and silver. From these metals they fashioned ornate vessels, ear ornaments, amulets, crowns, spoons, and knife blades.

The most impressive of the Inca skills, however, was engineering. They were able to build elaborate palaces and temples of carefully fitted stones even though they had no harder tools than those made of bronze. They terraced thousands of mountainsides to contain their farm lands, and they built complex ducts to water their crops.

In order to administer their enormous empire, the Incas had their engineers construct a skein of paved and cobbled roads equal to those of the Roman Empire. These roads extended for thousands of miles from Quito in Ecuador, along the ridge of the Central Andes, to Argentina and Chile. Other roads passed from west to east, beginning along the Pacific coast, scaling the high Andes, then dropping to the hot Brazilian jungles.

The engineering of these roads was incredible, for these highways crossed passes fourteen thousand feet high, tunneled beneath precipices, and spanned deep-flowing rivers like the raging Apurimac which Hiram Bingham had crossed on an Inca-style bridge. When Inca engineers encountered a river or deep gorge, they flung a suspension bridge across it. The bridge was usually constructed with five cables made of tough liana vines or braided strands of aloe fiber which were sometimes three hundred feet long. Three of the cables supported the floor of the bridge, the remaining two served as handrails. Since the cables got a lot of wear and tear, swaying alarmingly in the winds, and were subject to violent weather changes, they were changed every two years.

At the bridgeheads and at intervals of four to eight miles along all the major highways, the Inca engineers built *tampus,* combination inns and storehouses large enough to accommodate caravans of llamas bearing goods to the capital, and to put up traveling government officials. At each *tampu* were stationed two runners called *chasqui,* who relayed official government messages from post to post. They were said to carry messages 150 miles a day. In addition to the runners, the Incas had telegraphers stationed at intervals along the roads. By means of coded smoke signals they could transmit important information a distance of two thousand miles in two or three hours.

When Hiram Bingham and Clarence Hay were in

Cuzco, they frequently talked about the origin of the Inca people with the scholars at the University of Cuzco. Although Cuzco had once been the Inca capital, none of the scholars really knew where the Incas had come from, or how long they had been around. There were many legends on which to base rough guesses.

According to one legend, the first Incas entered the Cuzco valley from somewhere else. These first settlers were led by four brothers and four sisters who lived in caves, perhaps a day's walk southeast of Cuzco. Searching for good farm land, they carried with them a golden staff, which they kept poking into the ground to test the depth of the soil. Three of the brothers apparently dropped by the wayside, but the remaining one, Manco Capac, with his four sisters and followers, reached the valley, where they found the soil to be good. After driving out the local inhabitants, they founded the city of Cuzco. Manco Capac became its first ruler.

Another legend tells of a far older line of Peruvian kings called Amautas. The fifty-third of these kings, whose name was Huilcanota, established his capital at Cuzco. He and his sons ruled for many generations, but during the reign of Pachacuti, the sixty-fourth Amauta, barbarians invaded the land. Following a fierce battle, Pachacuti died from an arrow wound and his followers fled to a distant mountain fortress called Tampu-tocco.

According to the legend, these people and their descendants lived at Tampu-tocco for four hundred years before one of their leaders, again Manco Capac, felt strong enough to take them back to Cuzco. As in the first legend, Manco Capac set out with his brothers and sisters. When he reached Cuzco, he founded the Inca dynasty by marrying one of his sisters. Between Manco Capac's founding of the royal house and the Spanish Conquest, there were eleven Incas, or rulers.

Under the ninth Inca, Pachacuti Inca Yupanqui, the people of Cuzco began their great conquests, finally creating a vast political empire which united and controlled the extensive territory from northern Ecuador to the Río Maule in Chile—an empire with a population estimated to be from three to seven millions, and an area covering 380,000 square miles. It was a kind of Pax Romana in the New World where an all-powerful emperor governed a land that included some of the highest mountain ranges, most dense jungles, and greatest deserts in the world.

The Incas showed a genius for government and administration that was rare in pre-Hispanic America. The structure of the government was like a pyramid with the emperor at its apex. His proper titles were Sapa Inca, meaning the Unique Inca, and Intip Cori, meaning the Son of the Sun, because it was believed that he was a direct descendant of the sun. He was worshiped as a god during his lifetime and after his death. Although he was allowed to have numerous wives, his sister was his chief wife.

The royal court was made up of the emperor's sons and of nobles related to him by blood. These men ruled over the many provinces of the empire. To help them govern the distant regions, an administrative nobility was also created. These second-rank nobles were usually men who spoke Quichua, the language of the Incas. This nobility also included leaders of the nations and tribes which had been conquered and had become part of the empire. Such men were Incas by privilege and they could be distinguished from other Peruvians by the special headbands and large earplugs they wore. The earplugs caused the Spaniards to call them *Orejones*, Big Ears.

To rule over so many people, the Inca pyramid of government divided the population into units and subunits of families, each having an administrator–tax collector over it. The population was also divided into age groups, each group having certain duties and rights.

Women and girls were not exempt from these regulations. At regular intervals, an Inca official would visit each village to inspect all the girls who had reached the age of ten. Girls who were not especially good-looking were left in the villages, where they eventually married the local boys. The good-looking girls were sent to the larger cities to attend special state convent schools, which were called *Accla Huasi*, Houses of the Chosen Women. Some of these girls were sacrificed at special religious ceremonies; the others were taught skills— weaving, cooking ceremonial foods, embroidery, and the preparation of a ceremonial liquor. At the age of sixteen, the girls not picked for human sacrifices were again sorted out. The loveliest were chosen to be concubines of the emperor. Others were selected to become Virgins of the Sun and to serve in the temples. The least pretty were given to nobles and military captains who had distinguished themselves during the year.

The Inca emperor's absolute control over his people was made easy because of two beliefs held by all the people: one was economic, the other religious.

The ancient Peruvians, like all the other people of the

ancient Americas, had no idealistic beliefs about the sacredness of private property. Except for a few personal belongings, they felt that everything was the property of the emperor. In their world there was no such thing as money. Taxes were paid in produce or labor. People in a village or clan kept one third of what they made or grew for themselves; another third went to the government storehouses; the final third supported the priests and temples. In return, when the people suffered from famine or other disasters, the emperor came to the rescue, distributing goods and food from the government storehouses.

To keep exact records of all these transactions, the Incas developed a system of accounting with the *quipu*, which is sometimes still used in the Andean regions. The *quipu* is a finger-thick cord to which a series of knotted strings of various thicknesses and colors are attached. The special arrangement of the knots, their number, and their colors indicated quantities or numbers. At certain times of the year, tax collectors, accompanied by special accountants called *quipu-camayoc*, went out to the villages, where, after reading the *quipu* code, they reckoned how much work the villagers had done for the government, how large their harvest should be, or the number of miles they had traveled on government business. All this was deducted from the tribute that villages had to pay the emperor.

Although his control of all property helped the emperor maintain his absolute authority over the people, religion was a still stronger force. The people believed that there was an almighty god who had created everything, including lesser gods. This god, Viracocha, was rather distant from everyday affairs, and so the common people paid less attention to him than to the gods representing the sun, the moon, the winds, and other natural elements.

The people living in the high Andes, where the sun's rays are so important for warmth and for ripening crops, sought the favor of the sun-god. When they saw the days shorten and the sun move farther north, they feared that they would starve or freeze. When they watched the Priests of the Sun halt the sun's flight, during a ceremonial tying of the sun's rays to a stone nubbin in the temples, they believed it was a miracle. Thus the great sundials, the *intihuatanas* (places where the sun is tied), were among the most venerated Inca artifacts. And the emperor, representing the sun, was all-powerful.

Although the emperor seemed stronger than any other monarch on earth, there were certain weaknesses in the structure of his government. One of these was the lack of a fixed system of royal succession. The Incas had never decided on a method of naming the next emperor. When the Inca died, any of his sons by his chief wife could succeed him.

When the eleventh Inca emperor died in A.D. 1525, his two sons, Huascar and Atahualpa, fought for the throne. The result was a kind of civil war between nobles. When Atahualpa finally defeated his brother and imprisoned him at Cuzco, the split weakened the stability of the empire. Before the wounds could be healed, a mysterious band of men came up from the coast. They wore armor of metal and carried weapons that belched thunder and lightning. And they rode god-like beasts twice as large and many times stronger than Peruvian llamas.

In a matter of months the handful of strangers toppled the largest and strongest empire in the Americas.

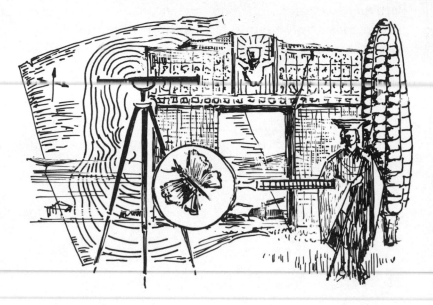

4.

DEATH OF AN EMPIRE

By the first quarter of the sixteenth century, Spaniards had rapidly established themselves in much of the new world discovered by Columbus. They settled and built cities on the larger Caribbean islands. Hernando Cortés had conquered the Aztec world and had explored as far as Honduras; Balboa had crossed the Isthmus of Panama to the Pacific; and the Atlantic coast of South America had been traced as far south as Río de la Plata.

In 1525 there were still a few blank spots on the maps of the New World. One of these was the tremendous empire of the Incas. Not a single Spaniard realized that millions of people in a highly organized state dominated by an all-powerful emperor lived on the continent. It remained for a tough, illiterate, overage soldier, Francisco Pizarro, to find the Incas and destroy them.

Pizarro was born in the bleak Extremadura region of Spain in the early 1470s. An illegitimate child, he received the upbringing of a peasant—hard blows and hard work. He never had an opportunity to attend school, and he never learned to read, write, or sign his name. Despite such drawbacks he became, for a short while, one of the richest and most powerful men of his century.

When Pizarro was in his early twenties, he somehow managed to make his way across the Atlantic to the newly discovered lands, where he took part in several expeditions. He accompanied Balboa on the expedition that discovered the Pacific. As a reward for his services, he was given a grant of land and Indian servants to work it. At this point he could have settled down to a life of ease; instead, he longed to discover and conquer new lands. Joining in partnership with another illiterate peasant, Diego de Almagro, he began the explorations of the west coast of South America. The partners, each over fifty years of age, were considered elderly men by the standards of their day.

Pushing their way through the unknown country along the coast of Colombia, they fought constant battles with Indians, who always outnumbered them. In one battle the small band of men was saved by an odd accident. Pizarro was knocked from his horse. The sight of the man falling from his horse, then remounting it,

47

stunned the Indians. They thought the horse was a strange four-legged beast with a human body growing from its back, and they were dismayed, thinking the beast had broken in half, then re-joined itself.

Suffering extreme hardships on the desolate beaches and in the rain-soaked jungles, Pizarro's men finally grew restless and insisted on returning to Panama. Reaching Gallo Island, just off the coast, they threatened to revolt. Tough, elderly Pizarro faced the demoralized men and drew a line upon the beach.

"You who wish to gain glory and wealth, step over the line to my side," he challenged his men. "Cowards, stay where you are."

The men hesitated. Finally one soldier stepped across the line; then another came, and another, until there were thirteen.

Months later, receiving fresh supplies and some reinforcements, the valiant thirteen continued down the coast to the edge of the Inca empire. From the coastal Indians they heard fanciful accounts of the wealth and power of the Incas. Pizarro swore his men to silence, then returned with them to Panama to organize a larger expedition. In 1528 he sailed to Spain, reported to the king, and received the appointment of Governor and Captain-General of Peru, a land he still had not seen. In January 1531, he set out for Panama with an expedition of three ships, 180 men and twenty-seven horses. He crossed the Isthmus, boarded new ships, and, with his tiny army, set out to conquer an empire of millions of people.

After many hardships Pizarro and his men reached the foot of the western cordillera. The stupendous wall of the Andes towered before them; and somewhere among those peaks lay an ancient city called Cajamarca where the Inca emperor, Atahualpa, was holding court.

By this time Pizarro had heard that there was a split between the two Inca brothers, and that Huascar had been defeated and was being held prisoner at Cuzco. Instead of following the comfortable high road to Cuzco, Pizarro decided to meet Atahualpa in the Inca's own camp. Leading his men up precipitous trails to the crest of the cordillera, he entered the beautiful mountain-ringed valley of Cajamarca on November 15, 1532.

Atahualpa was expecting the Spaniards; he had sent an ambassador to meet them. Nevertheless, he was uneasy. So he withdrew from the town which had a population of almost ten thousand inhabitants, and set up a royal camp on the far outskirts of the city.

Pizarro and his small band entered a deserted city. Wasting no time, Pizarro sent a small body of cavalry to contact the Inca. The cavalry group was led by Hernando, one of Pizarro's brothers, and by Hernando de Soto, who was the best horseman among the Spaniards. When they approached the Peruvian camp, De Soto treated the Inca emperor to a spectacular exhibition of horsemanship. He put his stallion through various maneuvers and capers, finally racing the horse directly at Atahualpa. When it appeared as if the horse would trample the emperor, De Soto brought him to a rearing, snorting halt, so close to the Inca that foam from the animal's mouth spattered the emperor's clothing.

Atahualpa had never seen so gigantic an animal. Although some of his nobles and soldiers were frightened by the equestrian exhibition, and fled, Atahualpa neither moved nor flinched; he maintained a marble composure.

A meeting between Pizarro and Atahualpa was arranged for the following day. On the eve of the meeting the Spaniards spent their free hours in typical conquistador fashion; they sharpened their swords and prayed.

At noon on the following day Atahualpa was carried to the appointed meeting place upon a golden throne which Pizarro's men described as "a gleaming castle of gold." The emperor was surrounded by nobles and soldiers dressed in richly ornamented garments. A canopy of gold cloth shaded the Inca from the sun, while vivid banners fluttered in the noon breeze. The Spanish chaplain stepped forward to deliver a glowing speech praising the glories of the Pope and the power of the Spanish king.

Suddenly, upon a prearranged signal, Pizarro and his men unsheathed their swords and attacked the unsuspecting Indians. The slaughter was terrible; hundreds of Inca nobles and Peruvian soldiers were killed in cold blood. Atahualpa was taken prisoner.

During his imprisonment at Cajamarca, he was treated as a reigning prince. No attempts were made by his own people to rescue him; however, Atahualpa made his own plans. He had shrewdly noticed the Spaniard's passion for gold, and one day he suggested to Pizarro that his people would completely fill a large room with a ransom in gold if the Spaniards would release him. Naturally, Pizarro agreed to this. During the next two months, to the amazement of the Spaniards, Indians came day after day from various parts of the country, bringing beautifully worked gold ornaments and vessels. Unable to appreciate the artistic value of these treasures, the uneducated adventurers promptly melted them down and cast them into gold bars. They were more interested in dividing the booty: one fifth for the Spanish crown, the rest to be divided among the invaders according to rank.

During this time Pizarro sent some of his men to Cuzco to see the imprisoned Huascar, as well as to find out how much support Huascar had among the Inca nobles. Fearing that the Spaniards might free Huascar and install him on the Inca throne, Atahualpa's friends in Cuzco murdered him. This needless crime played right into Pizarro's hands.

By now Pizarro had a fairly clear picture of how the Inca empire was put together. He realized that millions of Indians of all classes regarded Atahualpa as a god, the supreme ruler who commanded every aspect of their lives. Without his orders, no one knew what to do. Pizarro must have also realized that in the pyramid of government there were glaring weaknesses. All authority flowed downward from its apex, the emperor, but there was no contact between officials of equal rank, no sense of patriotism or of loyalty to each other. Pizarro knew that if he lopped off the top of the pyramid, the entire structure would fall to pieces.

Before marching to Cuzco he took that very precaution—he lopped off the apex of the pyramid. He put Atahualpa on trial. The hearing was an incredible, tragic farce. Atahualpa was charged with usurping the Inca throne and ordering the assassination of his brother. He was charged with squandering the public treasury (because he had had gold brought in for his ransom).

He was further charged with having too many wives. He was charged with idolatry and honoring false gods. Finally, he was charged with plotting an insurrection against the Spaniards.

He was found guilty and condemned to death. On the day following the mock-trial, he was baptized and given the Christian name John. A few minutes later he was executed by strangulation. With his death it appeared that the powerful Inca dynasty had reached its end— but not quite.

Pizarro, the self-made heir and ruler of the vast Inca empire, marched to Cuzco. Although he was not opposed when he entered the ancient capital, he soon realized that his little force was tremendously outnumbered. There were countless, proud Inca nobles in Cuzco and other cities who might make trouble. He prudently decided that he should set up a puppet Inca emperor to prevent the nobles and military chieftains from scattering and making trouble in the distant provinces.

Searching among the Incas of noble blood, he found a young man named Manco, who bore the same name as the legendary first Inca, and who was the grandson of the famous emperor Huayna Capac. Young Manco could be legally installed as the Inca ruler. And so Manco II was crowned with the scarlet *llautu*, or sacred fringe, the principal emblem of sovereignty among the Incas.

At first the young man was pleased, but as the months slipped by he sensed that he was the chief actor in a horrible comedy; he was a puppet obliged to obey the barbaric Spaniards. Instead of helping his people, he was helping the invaders enslave them. One day Manco, with his three sons and a number of loyal nobles, slipped away from the Spanish guards. Carrying the insignia of office and the sacred golden disc of the sun, Manco fled to the northern valleys.

Assembling a large army, he returned to Cuzco and began a siege that lasted several months. Cuzco was finally relieved by Pizarro's comrade, Almagro, and Manco retreated to the valley of Ollantaytambo, a favorite winter residence of the Incas. Here he made a determined stand, but Ollantaytambo was too easily reached by Pizarro's mounted cavaliers. In a bitter battle many of Manco's officers were killed; his favorite wife and his son, Titu Cusi, were captured. Manco and the remnants of his army fled to the northern wilds.

For Francisco Pizarro this was the last important battle against the Incas. He had secured his golden dream, but the dream was short-lived. In 1537 his old partner, Almagro, resenting Pizarro's superior position, challenged him. Both conquistadores were over sixty years old when they led their rival armies into battle. Although Almagro was defeated and executed by strangulation, Pizarro was still not secure. Four years after his partner's death, Pizarro was assassinated by some of Almagro's men.

One of Pizarro's brothers, a rough and tumble warrior named Gonzalo, stepped into the Captain-General's shoes. While he was busy trying to secure his position in Peru, word reached him that he had not heard the end of Manco. The Inca was creating an Indian kingdom somewhere in the mountains. It would threaten the Spaniards for forty years.

5.

THE VEST-POCKET EMPIRE

After seeing Choqquequirau, Hiram Bingham went to Lima and paid his respects to President Leguía who was extremely interested in his report. The Peruvian president suggested that he visit Carlos Romero, the nation's leading historian.

In Don Carlos Romero, Bingham finally found a man who agreed with his own feeling that Choqquequirau could not have been the last stronghold of Manco and his sons, during the forty years they maintained the remnants of the Inca empire after the Conquest.

"No one in Cuzco agrees with me," Hiram told the historian. "Dr. Giesecke, the President of the University of Cuzco; Dr. Aguilar; in fact, most of the staff hold to the Choqquequirau theory."

"I know how they feel," Don Carlos said, "but I am pleased with your conclusions. Simply because Paz Soldan and Antonio Raimondi said it was Choqquequirau, everyone in Cuzco believes it."

Don Carlos was referring to the noted Peruvian geographer, Paz Soldan, and to the Italian savant, Raimondi, who had spent a lifetime in Peru exploring every corner of the country in order to prepare his famous maps.

"I believe," said Don Carlos, "that Soldan and Raimondi took this position because various old Spanish chronicles mentioned that Manco had two strongholds: one called Viticos, which was near the present-day village of Pucyura; and the other, called Vilcabamba the Old. Although no Spaniard ever visited Vilcabamba the Old, it was said to be two or three days' hard journey from Viticos. Raimondi never found a Viticos nor a Vilcabamba, but it took him three days to travel from Pucyura to Choqquequirau; thus he decided Choqquequirau must be the Inca sanctuary, Vilcabamba el Viejo.

"Though no one seems to have found the ruins of Viticos and Vilcabamba," continued Don Carlos, "there is enough evidence in the Spanish chronicles to make me believe these places once existed. Choqquequirau is not one of them." He raised his finger dramatically, adding, "They are lost. They are still hidden somewhere in the mountains!"

The Peruvian scholar then showed Hiram Bingham

several important, very rare Spanish chronicles, which described Viticos and recorded the last days of Manco and his sons. He let Hiram transcribe key passages, and also gave him a list of Spanish documents which could be found in American libraries.

"Perhaps you will become sufficiently interested," said Don Carlos. "Perhaps you will return and search for the lost cities."

When Hiram Bingham finally returned to his family and his post at Yale, Don Carlos Romero's parting words continued to haunt him. Although he was extremely busy preparing reports about the Pan-American Scientific Congress, teaching, and writing the rough draft of a book about his recent trip to South America, he found time to piece together the story of Manco and his sons. Working late at night and in the small hours of the morning, he read the histories, the eyewitness reports written by Pizarro's conquistadores and the men who followed them to Peru. Sometimes he combed through a thousand pages of documents to find a single line about Manco or Viticos. He was like a detective putting together clues.

He became acquainted with some remarkable men— the authors of the Spanish chronicles.

One of the first of these men was Garcilaso Inca de la Vega who was born in Cuzco in 1539, just after the Spanish conquest. He was the son of an Inca princess and a Spanish conquistador. As a boy he knew some of the Pizarros, as well as one of Manco's sons. When his father, the Spanish governor of Cuzco, died, Garcilaso Inca de la Vega went to Spain, where he took part in the wars against the Italians and Moors, and then retired to a monastery. While a monk at Cordoba he wrote his *Royal Commentaries*, a fascinating history of the Incas.

Another Inca writer was Pachacuti Yamqui Salcamayhua, a grandson of the Incas, who had met most of the Spanish conquerors. His history of the Incas was to furnish Hiram Bingham with an important clue, helpful in identifying the lost sanctuary of Machu Picchu.

However, more important than the Inca historians were the Spanish soldiers, missionary friars, and viceregal secretaries who followed Pizarro and Almagro to Peru. Some, like Fernando Montesinos, who spent fifteen years in Peru as secretary to the viceroy, wrote enormous histories of the country. Montesinos' histories were based largely on the archives of the conquerors, plus his own fanciful embroidery. In one instance he enthusiastically traced the lineage of the Peruvian kings right back to Ophir, the grandson of Noah.

Other important historians like Pedro Cieza de León, who opposed Gonzalo Pizarro, played an active part in the politics of the conquerors. Still others, like Father Antonio de la Calancha, an Augustinian friar and son of a Spanish captain, recorded the experiences of the early missionaries. Calancha was born in Peru and became a priest at the age of fourteen. His thousand-page chronicle included reports made by other missionaries, particularly the stories of Father Marcos Garcia and a Father Diego, who actually lived for some years near Viticos and knew the last Inca lords.

These men, and others, their eyewitness accounts lost or forgotten in archives and libraries, furnished enough material so that Hiram Bingham was able to piece together a picture of how Manco II and his sons maintained a vest-pocket Inca "empire" deep in the Andes.

When the Spaniards drove Manco from Ollantaytambo, he fled down the Urubamba River until further passage was impossible because of the tortuous canyon and dangerous rapids. Turning northward into the region of soaring peaks and glaciers, he crossed the Panticalla Pass, which is over twelve thousand feet high, and finally shook off his pursuers. He then followed the Lucumayo River, which flowed into the Urubamba River just below the canyon area.

There are no records to tell what Manco did at this point. Most likely he went to the well-hidden sanctuary, Vilcabamba the Old, where he deposited the sacred golden sun disc in the Temple of the Sun. He probably rested there and planned his next moves.

When Manco was next heard of, he had crossed the Urubamba River and had gone up one of its tributaries, the Vilcabamba River, where he built a "long palace," or fortress, called Viticos. Here in the upper Vilcabamba Valley he created a strong base from which he could fight against the Spanish. The valley was sufficiently fertile to support a large population. It was remote enough so that Spanish cavalry could not easily penetrate it. It was also so situated that small bands of his soldiers could make swift raids on Spanish settlements, particularly on the great highway connecting Cuzco and Lima.

Manco's raids became so frequent and destructive that Pizarro sent several expeditions against him. The first expedition was commanded by Captain Villadiego, who followed Manco's original route of flight down the Urubamba and into the mountains. The exhausted Spaniards were ambushed in the Panticalla Pass; Captain Villadiego and all his men, except three, were killed.

Angered and alarmed by this defeat, Francisco Pizarro led a larger expedition, but he too was driven back. His brother, Gonzalo, tried his hand at capturing Manco, but was unsuccessful in penetrating the Inca's stronghold. Irritated by these failures, Francisco Pizarro vented his anger on a helpless prisoner. The colonial historian Montesino wrote: "Having taken one of Manco's wives prisoner with the other Indians, he stripped and flogged her, and then shot her to death with arrows."

In tracking down Manco's story, Hiram Bingham turned to the large collection of old and new maps he had gathered. The maps furnished a few fascinating clues, but they also added to his confusion. Studying the maps inch by inch with a strong reading glass, he tried to locate Viticos. On a rare map made in 1625 by the French cartographer De Laet, he located a Viticos. However, instead of indicating a village or a fortress, it represented an entire mountain province northeast of Lima. Measuring map distances with his caliper, he discovered that the province was 350 miles north of the Vilcabamba River which he had already located on several maps. Obviously, this could not be Manco's Viticos. Checking with later maps, it became clear that there was no province of Viticos because after A.D. 1750 it disappeared from Peruvian maps.

On Raimondi's great map of the region north of Cuzco, he found a village named Pucyura. Although that name did not appear in any of the Spanish chronicles, it struck him that it might be a modern spelling of Puquiura, which appeared often in the old records, and which was said to be near Viticos. Raimondi's Pucyura was in the upper Vilcabamba Valley, almost where Viticos was said to have been.

While studying the maps and reading the chronicles which were written in either Latin or sixteenth-century Spanish, Hiram ran into the disconcerting problem of Spanish spelling. In Quichua, the language of the Incas, there was no sound of V. Viticos and Vilcabamba were pronounced with the sound of U—Uiticos and Uilcabamba. Since early Spanish writers wrote the capital letter U like the capital letter V, or sometimes they used a capital B, Uiticos appeared sometimes as Viticos, as Piticos, as Biticos, and as Uiticos.

One night, after putting aside the maps and taking up the long history of the Augustinian missionaries, compiled by Father Calancha, he found in it an exciting document. It was entitled, *Report of the Conquest of Peru and the Acts of the Inca Manco II*. It had been dictated by Manco's son, Titu Cusi!

Titu Cusi was the boy who had been captured by the Spaniards at Ollantaytambo. He had been taken to Cuzco and held there for several years. With the help of Inca nobles living in Cuzco, he finally escaped, and although still a young boy, he joined his father at the "long palace" in Viticos.

In his report he told about his father's raids on the Spanish settlements. He gave some descriptions of

Viticos. He also drew a vivid picture of the first Spaniards to visit Viticos, and how they murdered his father.

During 1542 six Spaniards somehow crossed the Apurimac River with their horses, and appeared at Manco's headquarters. They were members of the band of men who had assassinated Francisco Pizarro. The leaders of the group, Gomez Perez and Diego Mendez, asked Manco to give them refuge. Since they were enemies of his enemies, the Pizarro brothers, Manco took them in and treated them kindly. They were given houses near the "long palace," and were provided with servants. They spent a great deal of time with Manco; they taught him horsemanship, as well as the use of Spanish firearms. To pass the time, they often played chess with him, or bowled and threw quoits on a green near the "long palace."

Manco, at this time, had agents in Cuzco who kept him informed of all that was happening among the Spaniards. One day his agents sent word that a new viceroy had come to Peru to clean up the mess created by the Pizarros. The viceroy had also brought the king's New Laws, which abolished the serfdom of all the Indians in the Americas. When Manco discussed the meaning of this with Gomez Perez, the latter suggested that Manco should write to the viceroy, offering his services to the king. "In this manner," said Perez, "you might recover your empire, or at least the best part of it."

Perez, accompanied by Indian servants and bodyguards, carried Manco's letter to the viceroy. The king's representative was so pleased by Manco's offer to make peace that he gave a full pardon to Perez and his friends, and sent Perez back as his emissary, loading him down with presents and messages of friendship for Manco. However, before any good came of the mission, a tragic argument ended Manco's life.

Titu Cusi, who was ten years old at the time, described the event thus:

In the said town of Viticos they were one day, with much good fellowship, playing at quoits with him; only them, my Father and me, who was then a boy. Without having any suspicion, although an Indian woman, named Banba, had said that the Spaniards wanted to murder the Inca, my Father was playing with them as usual. In this game, just as my father was raising the quoit to throw, they all rushed upon him with knives and daggers and swords.

My father, feeling himself wounded, strove to defend himself, but he was unarmed and alone. He fell to the ground covered with wounds, and they left him for dead. I, being a little boy, and seeing my Father treated in this manner, wanted to help him. But they turned furiously upon me, and hurled a lance which only just failed to kill me also. I was terrified and fled among some bushes. . . . At this moment the captain Rimachi Yupanqui arrived with some Antis warriors, and presently chased the Spaniards in such sort that, before they could get very far along a difficult road, they were caught and pulled from their horses. They all had to suffer very cruel deaths and some were burnt. Notwithstanding his wounds my father lived for three days.

Hiram Bingham found several other accounts of Manco's death in the works of Montesinos and Garcilaso Inca de la Vega. Although they differed somewhat in detail, they were agreed that the murder took place on the bowling or quoit green at Viticos. Manco's death occurred early in 1545.

Manco's eldest son, Sayri Tupac, now became the Inca ruler. Sayri Tupac had none of the vigor or daring of his father. He was a pleasure-loving young man who seemed not to resent the murder of his father by the Spaniards. Instead of leading his people against their enemies, he abandoned them. Against the advice of the Inca nobles at Viticos, he accepted the Spanish viceroy's invitation to leave the Inca stronghold and establish a kind of puppet royal court near Cuzco.

A short time after he became the Inca, he set out for Cuzco accompanied by three hundred Indian servants. He traveled with regal pomp and did a bit of sightseeing. He visited the Spanish viceroy in Lima, and then returned to Cuzco, where he lived for a short while in one of the old Inca palaces; finally, he retired to the beautiful Yucay valley. Although Sayri Tupac was a puppet in the hands of the Spanish, his image as the Son of the Sun (even though he had been baptized a Christian) was so powerful that no one thought of opposing the Spaniards as long as he was at peace with them. It took his death to change this.

6.

THE LAST OF THE INCAS

When Sayri Tupac died in 1560, Manco's youngest son,
Tupac Amaru, should have become the new Inca. However, since he was rather weak, and had passed most of
his years living among the Virgins of the Sun at a hidden
sanctuary (probably Vilcabamba the Old), the nobles
at Viticos were wary of him.

They favored Manco's second son, Titu Cusi. Although
he was an illegitimate son and had no legal right to the
throne, the nobles believed he was a stronger man than
Tupac Amaru. After all, he had witnessed the death of

64

his father and had no love for the Spaniards. Like his father, he too preferred the freedom of life in Viticos to living in the shadow of the Spaniards at Cuzco or Yucay. At the age of thirty, Titu Cusi was crowned with the red fringe of office at Viticos.

The young Inca had hardly stepped on the throne when he began to alarm the nobles. He allowed a Spaniard to visit him at Viticos. The visitor was the fearless Don Diego Rodriguez de Figueroa, an emissary of the viceroy, who left a vivid account of his trip to the vest-pocket empire. On May 12, 1565, he arrived at Viticos, where the first thing to catch his attention was the gruesome sight of the decapitated heads of Manco's murderers displayed on poles. Two days later he was taken to meet the Inca. His description of Titu Cusi is a memorable one.

Many lances were drawn up on the hill, and messengers arrived to say that the Inca was coming. Presently the escort of the Inca began to appear. . . . The Inca came in front of all, with a headdress of plumes of many colors, a silver plate on his chest, a golden shield in one hand, and a lance of gold. He wore garters of feathers and fastened to them were small wooden bells. On his head was a diadem and another around his neck. In one hand he had a gilded dagger, and he came in a mask of several colors. . . .

The Inca was a man of forty years [he was thirty], of middle height, and with some marks of smallpox on his face. His mien rather severe and manly. He wore a shirt of blue damask, and a mantle of very fine cloth. He is served on silver, and there are also twenty or thirty good-looking women, waiting behind him. He sent me to eat where he was with his women and his governor. The food consisted of maize, potatoes, small beans, and the other products of the country, except that there was very little meat, and what there was consisted of venison, fowls, macaws, and monkey, both boiled and roasted.

Rodriguez de Figueroa had a series of meetings with Titu Cusi. He tried to impress the Inca with the power of Spain; Titu, on the other hand, tried to impress him with the power of the Peruvians. Several times the Inca nobles staged mock battles in which they threatened the emissary's life, brandishing spears and clubs at him. Titu Cusi also put on several demonstrations. One day he had seven hundred Antis Indians march in review, while he brandished a spear and declared he could raise all the Indians in Peru against the Spaniards. Perhaps thinking that the parade of Amazonian Indians was not impressive enough, Titu Cusi sent for more troops.

When Rodriguez de Figueroa finally left Viticos, his secretary, Martín Pando, a man of Spanish and Indian parentage, stayed on in Viticos as the Inca's secretary. When the Spanish viceroy tried to send a larger mission to see Titu Cusi, the Inca broke off all relations with the Spaniards for almost five years. Martín Pando, however, finally convinced Titu Cusi that he should become a Christian so the Spaniards would not attack him. Titu dictated a letter to Father Juan de Vivero, prior of the

66

Augustinian order in Cuzco, requesting him to come in person to baptize him.

The prior stayed with Titu Cusi for seven days, instructing him in the Catholic faith. When the prior returned to Cuzco, he assigned one of his companions, Father Marcos Garcia, to remain with Titu Cusi and continue the instructions.

Father Marcos Garcia was a brave, but intolerant man. He was a hard-driving crusader, caring nothing for his own safety as long as he could convert Indians. Apparently, his constant harping and moralizing irritated Titu Cusi. The Inca refused to put the priest up at his court, but allowed him to build a mission church at a small village named Puquiura, which Father Marcos later wrote "was near Viticos where the Inca king held his court and his armies."

A short time later another Augustinian, Father Diego Ortiz, arrived in the region to assist Father Marcos. Although his appearance displeased Titu Cusi's advisers and nobles, Titu let him establish another mission at Huarancalla, about two days' distance from Puquiura. Father Diego was kind and sympathetic. The Indians admired him because he worked tirelessly to help them, treating their illnesses, teaching school, and helping in other ways.

Although Titu Cusi's nobles were worried about his acceptance of the foreign priests, Titu showed that he could make things difficult for the visitors. One day he became very irritated because Father Marcos had been pestering him about Vilcabamba the Old. The priest might have heard of it while working among the Indians

67

at the Capinota mission in the upper Urubamba valley. He called it Titu Cusi's "principal seat . . . the place where the Inca had a University of Idolatry where professors of witchcraft taught abominations." Titu Cusi agreed to take the priests to the mysterious sanctuary. The trip was truly an ordeal for them.

Father Marcos said that Titu Cusi traveled in comfort, riding on a royal litter borne by Indian carriers, while he and Father Diego made the difficult three-day journey on foot. At a place called Ungacacha, the priests were forced to walk waist-deep through icy water because the Inca had caused water from a nearby lake to flood the road. Watching the two friars struggle through the water, the Inca and his nobles laughed merrily.

When the travelers finally reached the vicinity of Vilcabamba the Old, Titu Cusi refused to take them to his "principal seat." The priests were kept under guard in an Indian village while the Inca and his followers went to the sanctuary. While Fathers Marcos and Diego were detained in the village for several days, they were subjected to unusual torture. According to Antonio de la Calancha, the Augustinian historian, Titu Cusi, realizing that the priests would not succumb to temptations of silver and gold, took another tack: "They must be subdued by being made to violate their vows of chastity." For three days the most beautiful girls from among the Virgins of the Sun were sent down from Vilcabamba the Old to tempt and entice the priests. They were dressed in the most tempting ways: some wore the garments of vestals, some wore the garments of princesses, and several came dressed as Roman Catholic nuns.

When Titu Cusi finally saw that the moral fiber of the

two priests could not be undermined, he took them back to the Viticos region. He put Father Marcos to work polishing the account of his father's life and death, which he had dictated to the secretary Martín Pando. This account, addressed to the Spanish king, was signed by Titu Cusi and witnessed by both priests in February 1570.

Shortly after this was done, Titu Cusi and his mother went back to Vilcabamba the Old. While he was there, Father Marcos decided that a daring operation should be undertaken to undermine the influence of the Inca priests in the region. He convinced Father Diego that they must destroy a local Temple of the Sun, which he later described as being "near a great white rock over a spring of water close to Viticos."

It took either great courage or foolhardiness to desecrate one of the principal shrines of the people they lived among. Father Marcos ordered his Indian converts to gather bundles of firewood. The two priests and their followers marched from the church at Puquiura to the Temple of the Sun "near the great white rock." They drove the priests from the temple area, and piled their firewood around the altar. A torch ignited the wood, and a roaring flame ravaged the site.

When Titu Cusi heard what had happened, he was furious. He hurried back to Viticos and ordered his men to stone Father Marcos out of the province, threatening him with death if he should ever return. Father Diego, beloved by the people, was spared, but he was never fully trusted again.

Not very long after the shrine-burning, Titu Cusi came down with a severe case of pneumonia. Father Diego, always ready to help, went to nurse him. Unfortunately, his simple herb medicines were not helpful and the Inca died. The year was 1571.

One of Titu Cusi's wives and the Spanish-hating nobles accused Father Diego of having poisoned the Inca. Both the good priest and Titu's secretary, Martín Pando, were tortured and put to death.

Immediately after Titu Cusi's funeral, Tupac Amaru, Manco's youngest son—the young man who had lived all his life among the Chosen Women, never learning the art of warfare or of ruling—received the red fringe of Inca sovereignty. His rule was brief because he had to deal with a new Spanish viceroy, Don Francisco de Toledo, a harsh, tough soldier who had no intention of giving in to the Incas.

Viceroy Toledo sent an ambassador to Tupac Amaru, either to persuade or order the young lord to move to Cuzco. Fearing that Tupac Amaru might give in to the viceroy, the Inca nobles sent warriors to ambush and kill the emissary. When he learned that his ambassador had been murdered, Don Francisco de Toledo declared war on the Incas. He offered a reward of one thousand pieces of gold for Tupac Amaru's head, and he sent a two-pronged expedition after the Inca.

One arm of the expedition went down the Apurimac River to cut off the Inca's flight if he went in that direction. The other arm, led by a Captain Garcia, who was married to a niece of Tupac Amaru, followed the traditional route to Viticos. Garcia led his men down the Urubamba River, over the Panticalla Pass, along the Lucumayo River, back to the Urubamba. They crossed the Urubamba on the Inca suspension bridge at Chuquichaca.

Marching up the valley of the Vilcabamba River, Garcia's men finally reached the upper valley. "Here," he said, "we came to the principal fortress, Guaynapucara, which the Incas had fortified. We found it defended by Prince Philip Quispetutio, son of the Inca Titu Cusi, with his captains and soldiers. It is on a high eminence surrounded with rugged crags and jungles, very dangerous to ascend and almost impregnable. Nevertheless, with my aforesaid company of soldiers I went up and gained the young fortress, but only with the greatest possible labor and danger."

But Tupac Amaru was not there. The young Inca's advisers had persuaded him to leave the region and go down the Pampaconas valley to a tropical retreat which Titu Cusi had built during his reign. Torturing the captured nobles, Garcia learned where Tupac Amaru had fled. He followed with relentless energy, driving deep into the jungle country, and finally took Tupac Amaru prisoner.

The young lord was carried back to Cuzco, where he was put on trial, a trial hardly different from the one to which Atahualpa had been subjected. Although this tragic young man had done nothing, except to run from the Spaniards, he was sentenced to death. He was forced to watch as his wife was torn to pieces before his eyes, and as his children were executed. Then he was beheaded.

Thus the Inca dynasty ended in 1572.

7.

AN EXPLORER'S CHECKLIST

As Hiram Bingham searched the old chronicles and ran his finger over old maps, he picked out what seemed to be key place names and descriptions. Sometimes it was a single word, at times an isolated line, or, when he was lucky, an entire paragraph—all of them clues that might help an explorer identify Viticos and Vilcabamba the Old. Had he noted them down, perhaps emphasizing the most important references, his checklist might have read as follows:

A) From Cieza de León:

1) "It was to the **province of Viticos** that Manco determined to retire when he rebelled against Pizarro, and that having reached **Viticos** with a great quantity of treasure collected from various parts, together with his women and retinue, the King, Manco Inca, established himself **in the strongest place he could find,** whence he sallied forth many times and in many directions, and disturbed those parts which were quiet, to do what harm he could to the Spaniards."

COMMENT: No province of Viticos appears on any old or modern map. . . . Does "strongest place" signify a fortress or an easily defended area? "Sallied forth in many directions" suggests a place central enough (with trails or roads?) from which to raid Spanish settlements and the Lima–Cuzco road. Could it be Choqquequirau?

B) From Captain Garcia:

1) When he pursued and captured the last Inca, Tupac Amaru, Garcia's route was: Down **Urubamba River to canyons,** over **Panticalla Pass, Lucumayo River to Urubamba River,** over the river via the **Chuquichaca suspension bridge,** then up Vilcabamba valley. He followed a **narrow trail with jungle on one side and a deep ravine on the other.** He stormed several small forts, then having arrived at "the **principal fortress, Guaynapucara,** which the Incas had fortified, etc. . . . **It is on a high eminence surrounded with rugged crags**

and jungles, very dangerous to ascend and almost impregnable. . . ."

COMMENT: No Guaynapucara on any map; nor is it mentioned in any other chronicle.

2) After capturing Guaynapucara, Garcia follows Tupac Amaru through **Huarancalla**, down the **Pampaconas** valley to the **Amazon jungle country.**

COMMENT: Huarancalla and Pampaconas appear on the Raimondi map. In another chronicle Pampaconas is described as **"a high, cold place . . . an important town of the Incas."**

C) From Baltazar de Ocampo:

1) Visited Viticos and gave reports of Titu Cusi's funeral. He said that at the funeral the Inca nobles **"proceeded to the House of the Sun, where was the Inca Tupac Amaru . . . with the Acllus under the Mama-cunas. . . ."** He also wrote that upon Manco's death, when Titu Cusi became the Inca, Titu Cusi "by his management and cunning kept his brother [Tupac Amaru] **secluded and imprisoned** on account of his want of experience."

COMMENT: Titu Cusi died at Viticos. Where was the funeral held? Did it begin there, and end at the House of the Sun, possibly Vilcabamba the Old, where Tupac Amaru and the Virgins of the Sun lived?

2) Ocampo describes the route to Viticos, saying, **"the road was narrow in the ascent with a forest on the right and on the left a ravine of great depth."**

COMMENT: This fits Captain Garcia's description. See Note B-1.

3) Ocampo describes Viticos, saying, **"The fortress of Piticos was on a very high mountain whence the view commanded a great part of the province of Vilcabamba."** He describes the fortress or "long palace," saying, "There is an **extensive level space with a very sumptuous, majestic building erected with great skill and art, all the lintels of the doors, the principal as well as the ordinary ones, being marble elaborately carved."**

COMMENT: Would the "extensive level space" be the bowling or quoit green where Manco was murdered?

4) Ocampo mentions a Vilcapampa, a village not far from Puquiura. He says, "To this city of San Francisco de la Victoria de Vilcapampa, when it was first peopled **after 1572,** there came the monks of Our Lady of Mercy and founded a convent. . . ."

COMMENT: This Vilcapampa (Vilcabamba) appears on modern maps, and it is not far from Pucyura. It was obviously founded after the last Incas. It probably is not Vilcabamba the Old.

D) From Titu Cusi:

1) Titu Cusi describes leaving Cuzco secretly, and going to **"Uticos** where my father [Manco] had come for fresh air, **it being a cold land."** He tells of the Spanish refugees, Gomez Perez and Diego Mendez, playing games with Manco: "In the said **town of Uticos,** they were one day, with much

75

good fellowship, playing at quoits with him." Then, after they murder Manco, they flee on their horses. "Before they could get very far along a **difficult road,** they were caught and pulled off. . . ." In his letter to the governor of Cuzco, Titu Cusi describes meeting the prior of the Augustinian order **"at Rayangalla** on the 12th of August, 1568, **whither I came from Vilcabamba . . ."**

COMMENT: There is no Rayangalla on any new or old map. Could this be Captain Garcia's Huarancalla, or might both of these be the present-day village of Huarancalque?

E) From Don Diego Rodriguez de Figueroa:

1) Don Diego leaves Cuzco, going to visit Titu Cusi in Viticos, via the route most often used: Ollantaytambo, Pass of Panticalla, Lucumayo River, the suspension bridge, etc. He is escorted to Viticos by Inca captains. Titu Cusi is not there. Don Diego goes out to meet him at a place where **"the Indians of Bambacona had made a large house on a strong height** surrounded by entrenchments. Below were the houses of the inhabitants. **The road by which he** [Titu Cusi] **was to come was very clean and passed over a great plain."**

COMMENT: Would this Bambacona be related to the Pampaconas valley that Captain Garcia went down when trailing Tupac Amaru? Keep in mind the "great plain."

2) During Don Diego's meeting with Titu Cusi the Inca sends **"to Vilcabamba for more men. . . .**

On the 25th of May, one of his generals arrived with three hundred men armed with lances . . . then a hundred captains of those who came from Vilcabamba, etc. . . ."

COMMENT: There is a seven- or eight-day period between the time Titu Cusi sent to Vilcabamba for soldiers, and their arrival. This can establish Vilcabamba as being three or four days' march from Titu's palace in Viticos.

3) During his meeting with Titu Cusi, Don Diego Rodriguez de Figueroa gave him various presents, including "silver bracelets, crystals, pearls, needles, two pair of scissors, and other Spanish things."

F) From the Calancha history (Father Marcos and Father Diego):

1) Calancha says, "The Province of Vilcabamba is a hot country of the Andes and is mountainous and includes parts that are very cold, intemperate, bleak uplands. It has hills of silver from which some quantity has been taken and it produces gold of which in those days much was found. . . . It is a land of moderate comfort, large rivers, and almost ordinary rains. It is a very large area covering fourteen degrees of longitude [about seven hundred miles wide]."

Concerning Father Marcos, he says, "Marcos built a church in Puquiura, two long days' journey from Vilcabamba. . . . Puquiura is the place in which the Inca king held his court and his armies. . . ."

77

When Father Diego came into the region, he built a church at the **village of "Guarancalla . . . It was a distance of two or three days' travel from one convent to the other."**

2) When the two priests destroyed the Inca's **"House of the Sun which was close to Viticos in a village called Chuquipalpa,"** the place seemed not more than a half-day walk from Father Marcos' church at Puquiura. The Inca shrine is described as having **"a white stone over a spring of water."** It was called **Yurak Rumi.**

3) When Titu Cusi agreed to take the two priests to **"Vilcabamba, his principal seat,"** and the priests were forced to walk through a flooded area, they called it **Ungacacha.**

COMMENT: Places bearing the names Chuquipalpa, Yurak Rumi, and Ungacacha do not appear on any map. In Quichua, *yurak* means white; *rumi* means rock or stone.

8.

HOW TO ORGANIZE AN EXPEDITION

Although he was intrigued by everything he had read about the Incas, Hiram Bingham was much too practical and much too busy to think of returning to Peru. However, during the summer of 1910, while he was working on the final details of his book, *Across South America*, he let a friend, Edward S. Harkness, read the publisher's galley proofs. Harkness was so interested by the description of the trip to Choqquequirau, and by what Bingham told him about the last Incas, that he asked, "Isn't it about time for an expedition there?"

The question startled Hiram. A quizzical smile crossed his lean face. "An expedition? To Peru?" he said. "Why, I've been so occupied, the thought of another trip right now hadn't crossed my mind."

Harkness then made a surprising suggestion. "Hiram, when you decide to make a trip there, let me know. I'll pay the expense of sending a geologist along with you."

The offer was like a tiny spark falling into the dry and ready tinder of Bingham's imagination. It began to smolder. . . . An expedition, not just a trip! But what kind of expedition? It must have some worthwhile purpose. Expeditions were costly affairs. He could not lead a group of men on a fanciful quest for a lost city; that was just too romantic.

For the moment he could think of nothing else but the lost Viticos. However, a few weeks later, something fanned the smoldering idea into flame. A magazine editor asked him to review Adolph Bandelier's new book, *The Islands of Titicaca and Koati*, which dealt with the Andean world. A footnote in the book caught Hiram's attention. It said that Mount Coropuna in Peru was over 23,000 feet high and was the culminating point on the continent. If Professor Bandelier is correct, thought Hiram, then the mountain is higher than Aconcagua. Most reference books listed Aconcagua, with its elevation of 22,763 feet, as the highest peak in the Western Hemisphere.

Now, something puzzled Hiram. He had traveled over a large part of Peru and had discussed Peruvian mountains with geographers and mountain climbers. He could rattle off the names of such snow-capped peaks as Salcantay, Veronica, Soray, and Soiroccoha, all of them soaring more than eighteen thousand to twenty thousand feet above sea level. Why hadn't he heard of Coropuna? He turned to his maps again. To his surprise, most of the maps, even recent ones, showed no Coropuna. Finally he located the peak on one of Antonio Raimondi's maps. It was situated in the Peruvian coastal range, lying due south of Choqquequirau. Raimondi listed it as twenty-six feet higher than Aconcagua.

An idea grew in his mind. Why shouldn't someone do a cross-section survey of Peru, following the line of the seventy-third meridian from the Pacific Ocean to the Amazon jungles? The line would take in Mount Coropuna, as well as crossing through the heart of the Andes, where the Inca, Manco II, had reigned over his vest-pocket empire. A Yale anthropological expedition had just returned from a season's work in this area and reported that it was one of the greatest unexplored regions in the world.

Hiram began to visualize a scientific expedition that would carefully map the region, and collect specimens of the flora and fauna, as well as search for Inca ruins. There should be at least four or five specialists in the party: an anthropologist-archaeologist to study the ruins and the people in the region, a naturalist, a geologist, a topographer-mapmaker, and a historian.

He began toying with a date. Already familiar with the seasons and the topography of Peru, he decided it would be best to begin exploring in June or July when rainfall was lightest. He would start his group working in the high country, then as the Peruvian summer set in (November), the expedition could move toward the coast to survey Mount Coropuna.

81

It is very easy to dream up an expedition, to decide how many men are needed, to plan the routes of travel, to whip up lists of equipment and supplies; however, to make a dream come true, one vital problem must be faced before anything can be set rolling. The problem is money. Hiram Bingham had some money, but not enough to pay the passage of five or six men back and forth to South America, let alone to pay all their other expenses and salaries. Who would finance the expedition?

During the fall of 1910 he found no solution to this troubling question. Then, while attending a class dinner at the Yale Club in New York, the answer dropped on his plate. During the dinner his classmates called on him to make a speech. Naturally, he spoke about his experiences in South America and his idea concerning an expedition. He told an anecdote about how he had been given counterfeit coins at the National Bank in Bolivia when he had traveled there in 1909.

"I forgot to bite them to see if they were good silver," he said. "But I am not the only one who received bad coins. Peru almost went to war against Bolivia because the Bolivian government was flooding South America with false coins." He smiled, and ruefully added, "If I could think of some way to finance an expedition with counterfeit coins . . ."

After the supper one of Hiram's classmates, Herbert Scheftel, approached him. "You don't need counterfeit coins, Hi," he said. "All you need is some friends at Yale. The expedition fascinates me. Why don't you make it a Yale Expedition and some of us will help you? Mr. Harkness offered to send a geologist. I'll foot the bill for a topographer."

Returning to Yale, Hiram began conferring with department chairmen and specialists in the fields related to the purpose of his planned expedition. Although the university could not provide funds on short notice, President Arthur T. Hadley sanctioned Bingham's attempt to raise funds for a Yale expedition to Peru. Hiram immediately began writing to friends, and friends of friends, for help.

One of his first letters was to Huntington Smith, Jr., who had accompanied him from Argentina to the Pan-American Scientific Congress in Chile.

Dear Coot:

. . . . Knowing your interest in the progress of exploration at Yale, and remembering your willingness to see me half way in adding books to the Yale Library, I am writing to ask you to help make this expedition a success by contributing one-third of its cost, or an amount equal to that which I shall contribute myself. My plans are these: I expect to leave New Haven the latter part of June and be gone six months . . . it is my plan to explore a section of Peru from the Sea Coast, across the Andes into the Amazon valley as far as is practicable. . . . I am convinced that there are more Inca ruins to be discovered in that locality, and particularly on the north slopes of the glacier-clad peaks which separate Choqquequirau from the Urubamba valley.

I figure that the expedition will cost about $5,000, including the salary of a topographer. . . .

Faithfully yours,
Hi.

Frequently there were "So Sorry" notes, but enough offers of support arrived for Hiram to begin making definite plans. To help keep down the expenses, since it began to look as if the project would cost far more than the five thousand dollars he had originally estimated, Hiram wrote to President Taft for the loan of government topographic and surveying equipment. Yale University gave two of its key scientists a leave of absence, with full pay, so they could accompany the expedition. At times help came from unexpected quarters. George Eastman of the Eastman Kodak Company offered to furnish each member of the expedition with a camera, field developing kits, and all the film that might be needed. Eastman was interested in having his new films and products tested under tough field conditions.

During the spring of 1911, the members of the exploring party were finally chosen. Yale University contributed four members: Professor Isaiah Bowman, a noted geologist and geographer who was given a leave of absence from his duties at the Peabody Museum; Professor Harry Foote, a naturalist at Yale's Sheffield Scientific Institute; Paul B. Lanius, an undergraduate at the Sheffield school; and Hiram Bingham. Since none of the Yale archaeologists was free to join the expedition, this post was filled by Herman Tucker, a husky twenty-seven-year-old archaeological engineer, who had just returned from a year of exploration in Alaska. The expedition's topographic engineer was Kai Hendriksen, a lively, witty Dane, who had studied at the University of Copenhagen and who had served as a civil engineer with the Royal Geodetic Survey. Although Hendriksen was now working with the U.S. Coast and Geodetic Survey, he was given a leave to join the Yale group. The expedition's surgeon was Doctor William Gage Erving of Washington, D.C.

The two months before the departure date for Peru were hectic for Hiram. When he was not busy purchasing tents and equipment, or discussing the merits of army biscuits versus pilot biscuits, he was conferring with shipping companies, corresponding with the President of Peru, or arranging for pack animals. Almost every detail of the expedition was carefully planned in advance. On April 24, Hiram wrote to Doctor Erving, who had been unable to attend a final meeting of the expedition's members:

Dear Billy:

I telegraphed you this morning to please get ready to sail for Peru on May 25th. . . . You will sail with one of our civil engineers and will go directly to Arequipa and Cuzco, arriving there two weeks ahead of the other four members of the expedition, with the object of securing proper men and mules for the purposes of the work. Upon arrival of the other members of the party an early start is to be made for the Urubamba Valley.

The geologist and the topographer will work together as party No. 1, for the next five months. Party No. 2, consists of the naturalist, whose work is chiefly as a collector. Party No. 3, consists of the engineer in charge of archaeological exploration. It is probable that you will be attached to Party No. 2, during a large part of your time, and that parties 2 and 3 will camp together quite frequently. . . .

Hi.

85

Leaving New York on June 8, aboard the United Fruit Company ship *Santa Marta*, Hiram Bingham, Professor Bowman, Professor Foote, Herman Tucker, and Paul Lanius soon arrived in Peru. Bingham discovered that some interesting changes had taken place since his last visit to the region. Señor Nuñez, who had urged him to visit Choqquequirau, had now become the prefect of Cuzco. Nuñez assigned a Sergeant Carrasco, of the Peruvian Army, to assist the party.

The most important and welcome change that had occurred in the region was a new road. The Peruvian government had, with great difficulty, completed a road down into the Urubamba River Valley, skirting the impassable canyon, and reaching the Vilcabamba River. The road had been built to serve the isolated plantations in that region. Its completion meant that the Yale expedition might not have to follow the old and dangerous Inca route, over the snowy Panticalla Pass.

While final preparations were being made for the journey, Hiram visited with many of the men in Cuzco who had plantations along the Urubamba River and in the Vilcabamba Valley. He questioned them about the place names he had picked from the Spanish chronicles: Vilcabamba El Viejo, Viticos, Puquiura, Yurak Rumi, and others. None of the planters had heard of any of the names. This was to be expected, because most of these men went to their plantations for only a month or two each year. All their dealings with the local natives were usually carried on through a plantation foreman.

One afternoon, however, while visiting with Don Cesare Lomellini, whose warehouse was the Cuzco base for the expedition, Hiram was introduced to a talkative old prospector.

"When you prospected along the Urubamba River, did you come upon any Inca ruins below Ollantaytambo?" Hiram asked him.

"Yes, Señor," replied the garrulous old man. "There are numerous ruins on Machu Picchu and on Huayna Picchu. They are much finer than the ruins at Choqquequirau."

Hiram became keenly interested. He had read about a place called "Huaina-Picchu or Matcho-Picchu," in the report made by the French explorer Charles Wiener. In 1875, the Frenchman had visited Ollantaytambo, where Indians had told him about some fine ruins named Huainapicchu. Although Wiener searched the area for months, he failed to find the ruins.

"Have you seen the ruins?" Hiram asked the prospector.

"Well, Señor, no. It is very difficult country."

"How do you know about Huayna Picchu?"

"An Indian once told me. He said the ruins were on the top of Huayna Picchu, a very high, inaccessible peak."

"Had the Indian who told you about it seen Choqquequirau?"

"I do not know, Señor."

"Have you seen Choqquequirau?" Hiram asked.

"No. I have not been there."

After the prospector departed, Hiram glanced questioningly at Señor Lomellini. "What do you think, Don Cesare?" he asked.

The Italian merchant shrugged, saying, "He is an old man. Most people in Cuzco laugh at his stories and have little confidence in him. Too often he has brought back reports of rich gold mines which did not pan out. Nevertheless, it might be worth investigating. The new government road passes very close to Huayna Picchu."

Early in July the expedition got underway, following the road leading across the arid Cuzco plain toward the distant rim of mountains. At about a league out from the city, the expedition caravan stopped at a bend in the road for a last view of the city. Here they noticed that the Indian travelers on the road, both those leaving and those coming toward the city, also paused, removed their hats, and prayed while looking toward their Mecca. Even in this, the twentieth century, the Peruvian Indians still looked upon Cuzco as a holy city.

Continuing on, the expedition reached a place where the plateau seemed to fall away suddenly, revealing a beautiful valley some three thousand feet below. This was the upper Urubamba valley, a place noted for its pleasant climate, beautiful gardens, and brilliant flowers.

"This is the valley called Yucay," Hiram told Professor Foote. "It was here that Manco's eldest son, the Inca Sayri Tupac, came to live after leaving Viticos. He died here."

They stopped in the first village in the valley, a town called Urubamba. The following day they pushed on to Ollantaytambo. On the hills surrounding the town, there were impressive Inca ruins which the party investigated and mapped. On one hill there was a large fortress with great granite slabs that weighed from fifteen to twenty tons. On another cliff there were buildings which the Cuzco antiquarians believed had been an Inca prison. They said that prisoners sentenced to death were flung over the cliff.

Continuing along the new government road, Hiram and his companions were amused by the kind of traffic they encountered. As yet, no cars or trucks utilized the narrow, twisting road. Occasionally, they passed a wagon pulled by mules. Traffic, on this highway, meant passing a llama pack train or a mule train, perhaps once every other day. With each new day of travel, the region became more interesting. There were magnificent, wild vistas, and, at the same time, many signs that this valley had supported a large Inca population: ruins of isolated fortresses, stone terraces, and other reminders of the past.

At the village of Qquente a base camp was established, and the expedition split into its specialized parties, each beginning its own investigations. Herman Tucker and Paul Lanius crossed the Urubamba River to investigate some important-looking ruins, situated on high terraces. Professor Bowman and Kai Hendriksen began surveying the region, in order to prepare a map of the river valley. Harry Foote wandered off with his butterfly net, bottles of chloroform, and cardboard boxes, to collect insect specimens.

Although the ruins across the river were extensive, they fitted none of the descriptions of Viticos which Hiram had assembled. The Indians in the area called the place Patallacta, meaning a town on a high terrace. The architecture of the ruins was late Inca. Hiram thought the place might have been occupied at the time of the Spanish conquest of Peru. It may have been abandoned around 1573, when the viceroy, Toledo, slaughtered a large part of the Inca population to make sure there would be no further vest-pocket empires.

Acting as scouts for the expedition, Bingham, Doctor Erving, Harry Foote, and Sergeant Carrasco continued downriver to Torontoy, the gateway of the Grand Canyon of the Urubamba. They entered a breathtakingly beautiful wonderland, the region behind the ranges— where something was lost and waiting.

The canyon reminded Hiram of vistas he had seen in the Canadian Rockies, and along the Koolan Ditch trail in Hawaii. Here the new government road slashed through the canyon, cutting recklessly up and down rock stairways and beneath granite precipices. One of the most amazing things, however, was that even in this wild area there were frequent signs of Inca occupancy.

Years later Hiram described his feelings about the region:

Emotions came thick and fast. We marveled at the exquisite pains with which the ancient folk had rescued incredibly narrow strips of arable land from the tumbling rapids. How could they ever have managed to build a retaining wall of heavy stones along the very edge of the dangerous river, which is death to cross! On one slight bend near a foaming waterfall some Inca chief had built a temple whose walls tantalize the traveler. He must pass within pistol shot of the interesting ruins, unable to ford the intervening rapids. High up on the side of the canyon, several thousand feet above this tem-

90

*ple are the ruins of Corihuayrachina . . . possibly
an ancient Inca gold mine.*

The travelers finally reached a place called La Maquina, where, today, the narrow-gauge railway from Cuzco ends its run. They came to a dirty thatch hut which served as an inn for travelers along this road. Doctor Erving poked his head inside, then immediately pulled back. "Too dirty," he said. "Much too dirty. Better pitch our tent outside somewhere."

Since there was no suitable place to pitch the tent, or to graze the pack animals, the party continued along a very difficult path until it reached a tiny clearing near the river. They pitched camp along a small sandy beach. In the evening twilight Hiram located their position on his map.

"Mandor Pampa," he said. The name amused him. The tiny clearing, perhaps two acres in size, had the gall to be called a pampa. He had seen the great pampas or grasslands of Argentina, where thousands of wild horses raced for miles without encountering hill or tree.

While Hiram and Harry were putting up the tent and Doctor Erving, the party's chief cook, got a supper fire going, a stranger edged into the camp area. The intruder was a short, brown-skinned, narrow-faced man. Sergeant Carrasco, always alert for trouble, confronted the man, asking what he wanted.

The stranger replied in Quichua that his name was Melchor Arteaga. He was the owner of the thatch hut back along the road. He was also the man who farmed Mandor Pampa. Arteaga was extremely suspicious. He wanted to know why the men on this expedition did not stay at his hut like respectable travelers. Sergeant Carrasco and Arteaga talked for some time, but suddenly the sergeant broke off the conversation and addressed Hiram Bingham.

"He says there are good Inca ruins across the river."

"How good?" asked Hiram.

"He says they are large, very large. They are on top of a mountain called Huayna Picchu. He says there are other ruins on a ridge called Machu Picchu."

"Has he seen the ruins himself?" Hiram asked.

Carrasco put the question to Arteaga. Although the latter said he had seen the ruins, and could lead the travelers there, he was rather vague about the size of the ruins.

"Will he lead us there?" Hiram asked.

Carrasco again questioned Arteaga, and translated. "He can take you there tomorrow, but he wishes to know what you will pay him."

"How much does he want?" Hiram asked.

Again Carrasco and Arteaga conferred, then the sergeant said, "He asks fifty cents a day. He says the trail is very difficult, so he must have fifty cents."

"Very well," Hiram agreed. "Tomorrow morning we'll look at this Huayna Picchu or Machu Picchu. We'll see if it is a myth or real."

9.

STUMBLING UPON A LOST CITY

The following morning, July 24th, Hiram Bingham had trouble getting together a party to climb Machu Picchu. The day was a dreary one. A steady, cold drizzle was falling. Billy Erving pushed back the tent flap, looked at the wedge of gray sky above the canyon, and shook his head. "I think I'll just dawdle around camp, Hi, if you don't mind. I've got to catch up on my laundry."

Harry Foote had his own excuse for not going along. "I think I'll fool around down here," he said. "I spotted some fascinating butterflies down by the river. I really ought to get them for our collection."

When Hiram and Sergeant Carrasco went to Arteaga's hut, their prospective guide was in the same sort of mood. He shivered, and peered out through the doorway at the gray drizzle, saying, "It is too hard a climb for such a wet day."

"Tell him I'll pay him a sol for guiding us," said Hiram.

Arteaga hesitated for a moment, then gave in. The offer of a Peruvian sol, or silver dollar, was too much to resist. It was several times the daily wage a man could earn in this region.

Finally, at ten in the morning, the three men set out, going back along the road for an hour, then turning off through the jungle to the river. They came to a primitive bridge made of logs resting precariously on boulders in midstream. The overnight rain had caused the river to rise; the turbulent water sprayed the logs, soaking them, and making them slippery. Arteaga and Carrasco took off their shoes to get a better footing as they inched their way across the bridge.

It was now Hiram's turn to cross. He hesitated for a moment, thinking that Harry Foote and Billy Erving had been quite wise to remain at camp. A single slip upon the bridge and he would tumble into the icy water, where he would be dashed to death against the boulders in the swift stream. Getting a grip on his nerves, he moved out upon the slippery bridge. "I am frank to confess," he said later, "I got down on my hands and knees and crawled across, six inches at a time."

Such caution was the better part of valor, because

an Indian boy, accompanying Bingham's second expedition to this region, slipped into the river at almost this same spot. His body was never found.

Now, cutting their way with machetes through the dense jungle along the edge of the river, the three men finally came to a steep slope. For more than an hour they climbed through the tangled brush and rain-slick grass, clawing for handholds, pulling themselves over rock outcrops. Arteaga, in the lead, began complaining.

"What is he fretting about?" Hiram asked Carrasco.

"Snakes," replied the sergeant. "He says this is the area where there are a lot of snakes."

"What kind of snakes?"

"Vipers. Here they are called fer-de-lance."

In spite of the heat and humidity, Hiram felt his skin grow cold. The lance-headed yellow viper, or fer-de-lance, was one of the most deadly snakes of the tropics, and could kill a man in a matter of minutes.

Climbing for still another hour, the exhausted men finally came to a level mountain shoulder about two thousand feet above the river. Arteaga led the way to a grass-covered hut, where, to Hiram's surprise, two Indian men and a small boy greeted them in Quichua and offered them gourds filled with cool, refreshing water, as well as some cooked sweet potatoes. There was a rustic log bench at the shoulder's edge. The Indians spread soft woolen ponchos upon it, so the travelers could rest and enjoy the spectacular view: the tremendous green precipices falling away to the thin silvery chain of the river far below; a great granite cliff directly ahead, rising a sheer two thousand feet; and to the left, a solitary peak surrounded by inaccessible slopes. That peak must be Huayna Picchu, Hiram thought. Unfortunately, he could see no signs of ruins.

While they rested, Carrasco had been chatting steadily with the two Indians, who seemed unusually friendly and ready to laugh at almost anything. Carrasco explained that their names were Richarte and Alvarez. He told Hiram that these men and the boy had been living on this mountain shoulder for almost four years. They farmed small terraces of land, where they grew maize, sweet and white potatoes, sugar cane, and tree tomatoes.

"How do they go up and down this slope?" Hiram asked. "Do they have some easier route?"

"They say there are two paths," replied Carrasco. "There is the one we followed, and there is another, more difficult path. The other path goes down the face of the mountain, but on the other side. They only use that one when the river rises and washes away our bridge. However, they do not go down very often. They are happy up here in the clouds."

"Have you asked them about Inca ruins?"

Carrasco nodded. "Yes, they say there are ruins toward the other end of this ridge."

"Far?"

"They say they are a little farther, but who knows?"

Rested and refreshed, Hiram was now ready to search for the ruins. When he stood up, Arteaga and the two Indians made no move to go along. "He says he has seen the ruins," Carrasco translated. "He will remain here to chat with his friends. The boy will show us the way."

The response of these men disturbed Hiram. Their interest in the ruins, if any ruins existed, seemed so negative that he felt certain they could not be important. Perhaps there was nothing more interesting up here than an isolated Inca lookout post or signal tower. The little Indian boy, hopping and skipping ahead, hardly seemed to augur the finding of any great ruins.

After following the boy some distance up the ridge, and going around a promontory, Hiram caught sight of a series of handsome stone terraces. Each terrace was about one hundred feet long and ten feet high. They had been cleared of trees. Apparently Richarte and Alvarez planted their crops here. The little boy, the most silent guide Hiram had ever had, led the way along one of the terraces, and then into a heavily wooded section.

Suddenly, beneath the deep shadows of the trees, Hiram spied the walls of ruined buildings. Although the structures were almost lost in the tangle of brush, and half-hidden by centuries of accumulated leaves and moss, he could see that the walls were beautifully con-structed. The little boy, sensing Hiram's excitement, hurried on. Hiram and the sergeant struggled through the bamboo growths and vines, until the boy led them to a cave that was walled with finely cut stone.

Above the cave stood a building, semicircular in shape, its walls following the curve of the rock below. It was connected to another wall, made of carefully matched blocks of pure white granite which seemed to have been selected for their fine grain. Hiram gave an exclamation of awe. "What superb work," he murmured. "It must have been done by a master craftsman. The workmanship is as fine as on any Greek temple."

The little guide motioned for him to hurry on. The boy scrambled up a steep hill and went up a rubbish-covered flight of stone steps. Now, surprise after surprise came in bewildering succession. The boy led the way up an impressive stairway made of large granite blocks, to the ruins of two buildings which were the finest and most interesting structures Hiram had seen anywhere in the Inca world. One of the buildings had walls twelve feet high. In one of these walls there were carefully cut niches and, beneath the niches, an exquisitely cut, oblong block, about fourteen feet long.

As he ran his hand along the block, Hiram said, "These buildings could have been a temple area. This might have been an altar, or if not an altar, a throne for the mummies. The Incas were ancestor worshippers; for certain religious ceremonies, they brought out the mummies of departed Incas."

For a moment he tried to visualize what it must have been like in this lonely, mountaintop sanctuary, at the time of Manco or Titu Cusi. He could see the vividly dressed Inca and his nobles, the priests, and the Virgins of the Sun gathered together here. The priest, in his resplendent robes of office, faced the east, greeting the rising sun, extending his hand toward it, throwing kisses to the sun. Somewhere up here, there must be an *intihuatana,* one of the sacred Inca sundials to which the Inca priests tied the sun.

Across a courtyard from the building with the long altar, or throne, was a still more striking building. Although it was roofless, as were all the other buildings, this one had a massive stone wall, framing three great windows that looked out over the great canyon below. In all his travels through Peru and Bolivia, Hiram had seen no other Inca building with so strange an arrangement of windows. Because of the high altitude and bitter cold winters, Inca and Indian buildings rarely had windows. If there were any at all, they were usually small and easy to cover.

There must be some special significance, he thought. The windows must mean something.

Again the little, barefoot guide urged Hiram and the sergeant to follow him. He was enjoying the surprise and wonder shown by these two grown men, concerning this cloud-shrouded citadel which was his private playground. He led the strangers through more and more ruins. Of course, he could not show them everything at its best. The clouds and the drizzle hid the marvelous vistas of the ruins. Also, many of the buildings were buried beneath tangles of jungle growth.

Having taken what pictures he could in the gray weather, Hiram now began searching for landmarks, such as those mentioned in the old chronicles: a long palace with lintels of marble; a great white rock with a spring beneath it; perhaps a nunnery where the Chosen Women might have been housed. He had Sergeant Carrasco question the boy about such places, but the lad seemed unable to understand what was meant or wanted.

Before leaving the mountain peak, Hiram returned once more to the Temple of the Three Windows. He had decided it must be a temple. The unusual windows faced upon the spectacular canyon, but more important, they faced the east. Were they meant to catch the first rays of the rising sun, the giver of heat and light, so important in the religion of the Incas? Although he was not an expert concerning Inca customs and beliefs, he felt sure this building had some ceremonial purpose.

While looking at the distant, snow-clad mountains framed by the windows, the irony of his finding this remarkable place dawned on him. No one in Cuzco or Lima had ever spoken of the marvelous architecture on this almost forgotten mountain ridge. Why had every explorer since Pizarro missed it? Then he realized that he himself might have missed it. What if Melchor Arteaga had not really wanted the Peruvian sol for his day's wage, and had refused to leave his hut?

10.

THE LONG PALACE

For three days following the discovery, Hiram Bingham,
Harry Foote, and Billy Erving spent all their time poking among the mountaintop Inca ruins, making rough
sketches and cataloguing what they found. Over their
evening campfires they argued with each other, trying
to determine what the ruins could be.

"The place seems to fit the descriptions given by
Baltazar de Ocampo and Captain Garcia," said Doctor
Erving. "They described Viticos as being on a high
mountain, and with a view commanding the whole prov-

101

ince. They talked about majestic buildings. We certainly have the mountain, the view, the handsome buildings. Could Picchu simply be a twisting of the name Viticos or Piticos?"

Hiram shook his head. "I am beginning to doubt that this is their Viticos," he said. "Remember, they described a long palace with lintels made of marble. There is no really long building here, nor is there any marble."

"I don't think we'll find any marble anywhere," Harry Foote suggested. "If I remember correctly, in his geography Raimondi said he found no marble at all in this province. I think what happened was that those men, Garcia and Baltazar de Ocampo, were soldiers, not geologists. They mistook the white granite we see everywhere, for marble."

"You're probably right, Harry," said Hiram. "We have found something here, something very important. I don't think it is Viticos."

"What is it then?" asked Erving.

Hiram shrugged, saying, "I don't know. I've read nothing in the chronicles that seems to describe it. It might be Vilcabamba the Old. No Spaniard ever saw it."

"Well, it ought to have a name," said Harry Foote.

"If it had been occupied from ancient times to the present, like Cuzco or Ollantaytambo, then it might have preserved its ancient name," Hiram mused. "But I suppose it has been abandoned for centuries. Perhaps we'll never know what it was called. We might as well call it Machu Picchu, after the mountain it crowns."

Having given the mountain citadel a name, Hiram was anxious to continue the search for Viticos. He would turn Machu Picchu over to his companions for further

102

study. After sending one of the mule skinners with a note to Herman Tucker, ordering his party to do a careful topographic survey and map of Machu Picchu, Hiram's small group set out along the government road toward the lower Urubamba and the Vilcabamba Rivers.

At each plantation and at every small settlement he made inquiries about Inca ruins. He offered cash prizes to Indians for information about Inca ruins which might fit the description of Viticos and Yurak Rumi. When he reached the princely three-hundred-year-old plantation belonging to the Vargas family, whom he had met in Cuzco, he was given an exciting clue.

While enjoying the wonderful hospitality of the Vargases, Hiram told his hosts about the remarkable ruins he had found on Machu Picchu. They were stunned by this, finding it almost unbelievable, because in going back and forth to Cuzco they passed within a stone's throw of the mountain, without ever hearing that there were extensive ruins on it. When he showed them excerpts from the old Spanish chronicles, and told them about his search for Viticos and the spring with the white rock over it, they became enthusiastic about the quest. They assembled all the Indians working on their plantation so Hiram could question them. One of the mestizo foremen had heard of a Yurak Rumi.

"It is some distance down the river, on a ridge along the Salcantay Valley," said the man. "I have seen ruins there. It was many years ago. My workmen called the place Yurak Rumi."

"Was there a white rock and a spring?" Hiram asked excitedly.

"I do not know, Señor. There is much forest."

"Can I go there?"

"It is difficult, Señor. A trail must be cut to it."

The Vargas family was so excited by this information that they ordered a large work crew to hack a trail through the jungle. Although the trail was completed in a week, the effort was wasted, because the explorers found only a crudely fashioned stone hut—no white rock, no spring, no Temple of the Sun.

Continuing down the government road, the travelers came to a place where the Urubamba narrowed into a gorge. The government had built a bridge across the river at this point, which the natives of the region called Chuquichaca. This was the place where, centuries ago, the Incas maintained a suspension bridge, over which Manco and later Captain Garcia and Baltazar de Ocampo crossed on their way to Viticos.

Not far from the bridge, Hiram Bingham's party stopped at the Santa Ana plantation, which was owned by an elderly Colombian, Don Pedro Duque, who welcomed the travelers with warm hospitality. Don Pedro, a well-educated man, became keenly interested in their work. After reading Hiram's extracts from the chronicles, he sent out messengers, inviting friends to come to the hacienda and share their knowledge of the region with the explorers.

Although Duque's friends were unfamiliar with any of the names Hiram mentioned, one of them pointed to a spot on Hiram's map. "Conseirvidayoc," he said. "I think that might be Vilcabamba the Old."

"Eight years ago a man named Lopez Torres was down there looking for rubber trees," Don Pedro added. "He reported coming upon some ruins, but who knows what they are like. It is a terrible place to go. The jungle is dense. No one now living has been there. The region is inhabited by Indians who will not let strangers enter their villages."

Another of Don Pedro's friends, a crusty old man named Evaristo Mogrovejo, showed little interest in what the explorers were doing, until he discovered that Hiram had been to Choqquequirau.

"My brother, Pio Mogrovejo, was one of those who searched for buried treasures there twenty-six years ago," he said. "Now, why didn't you tell me you are looking for buried treasures? You plan to travel up the Vilcabamba Valley? Well, gentlemen, come to my village, Lucma. I am governor there. I have Indians who know the region well. We'll search for treasures."

"We're not interested in buried gold and silver," Hiram explained. "We're interested in ancient ruins."

"Bah"—the old man expressed his disgust. "Ruins—there are hundreds up the valley. They have no value."

A few days after this interview, the travelers set out for Lucma, where they planned to meet the old man and enjoy his knowledge of the country. When they set out, by accident—a fortunate one—Sergeant Carrasco took the wrong turn. Instead of going up the new road along the Vilcabamba River, he followed an older trail. To Hiram Bingham's delight, it exactly fitted Baltazar de Ocampo's description of the route he had taken from the Urubamba to Viticos. "The road was narrow in the ascent with a forest on the right and on the left a ravine of great depth."

Arriving in Lucma, a picturesque village with thatch-roofed huts, two stores, and a church with a pretty

105

tower, the travelers found that Evaristo Mogrovejo had kept his promise. He had called together the villagers and gathered information concerning ruins in the region. To make sure that nothing of importance would be overlooked, Hiram offered a Peruvian sol for every ruin to which he was led, and he offered to double the money if the ruin proved interesting.

The next day, guided by one of the villagers, the party climbed up a narrow ravine to a ridge that divided the lower Vilcabamba valley from the upper valley. Since the ridge seemed like an appropriate defense position, Hiram was not surprised when the guide led them to an Inca ruin situated on an artificial terrace.

"What do they call this place?" Hiram asked.

"The Indians call it Incahuarancana."

"In Quichua," said Sergeant Carrasco, "that means place where the Inca shoots with a sling."

Hiram nodded. The name was very apt. One of the chief weapons of the ancient Incas was the sling, which flung stones at an enemy with great power and accuracy. The Spanish conquistadores had reported that the Incas could smash a man's head or bring down a horse with a stone from one of their slings. And this place, of course, was ideal as a defense point.

"Incahuarancana . . . Inca Huarancana . . . that sounds like Huarancalla," said Billy Erving. "Didn't Captain Garcia say he came to a Huarancalla and stormed some Inca forts, while he pursued the last Inca?"

"Not quite," Bingham replied. "Captain Garcia's Huarancalla came after he had captured the principal fortress, Guaynapucara."

106

The Indian guide led the travelers on to another ruin, then to another. Although these ruins had surely been fortresses, none of them appeared to fit the descriptions of the fortress of Viticos with its marble lintels. Hiram decided that these must be the smaller forts, which Captain Garcia said he had stormed and captured before reaching the principal fortress.

Since there seemed to be nothing more of importance around Lucma, on the following day the explorers followed the river upstream until they reached a place offering them a clear view of the upper valley. Here, while relaxing in his saddle, Harry Foote spied a peculiar, flat-topped hill in the distance.

"That's an odd-looking formation," he said. "It seems quite steep and rocky—a fine place for a fort."

Evaristo Mogrovejo nodded. "That is Rosaspata. There are ruins on it."

"Have you seen the ruins?" Hiram asked.

"No, Señor, but the Indians say there are ruins. Some of the people at Pucyura have seen them."

"Did you say Puquiura?" Hiram asked quickly.

"Sí, Señor, Pucyura. When we ride a little farther you will see the town. It is at the foot of the hill, and across the river."

By noon they reached Pucyura, a prosperous village with a crumbling church and a well-built government school. As Hiram gazed at the church and school, he wondered if he had at last reached the Puquiura where the Augustinian priest Father Marcos Garcia had founded the region's first chapel and school, centuries ago. He could almost see the two priests, Father Marcos and Father Diego, leading their Indian converts along

107

this street, on their way to set fire to the Temple of the Sun. If Pucyura were the old Puquiura, then Manco's Viticos and Yurak Rumi must be within walking distance.

Too excited to rest after their midday dinner, the explorers set out for Rosaspata. They paused briefly to look at some ruins, which turned out to be Spanish rather than Inca, then began the stiff climb up Rosaspata. Working their way up the least craggy side of the hill, they soon came to an Inca wall. It was so carefully constructed and so smooth, it was obvious that no one could scale it. There was not a toe or finger hold on its surface.

"A half dozen Incas could have defended this point against an army," Hiram observed.

Finally reaching the crest, from which there was a magnificent view of the entire province, the travelers spied a most remarkable Inca building. It was tremendous in size, actually 245 feet by 43 feet, and it had fifteen doorways in front, as well as fifteen in back. When Hiram saw it, he instantly felt it was a fitting palace for an Inca king. He blurted out Baltazar de Ocampo's description. "There it is, 'erected with great skill and art, all the lintels of the doors, the principal as well as the ordinary ones, being marble elaborately carved.'"

"They're white granite," Harry Foote observed dryly, "and they are not carved."

"No, not carved in our sense of being sculptured," Hiram replied. "But they certainly are beautifully cut."

Although the ruins atop Rosaspata had been badly

treated—possibly by treasure hunters, and people from Pucyura who found the stone blocks nicely cut and useful for building—Hiram Bingham found enough evidence to make him believe he had at last located Viticos. Among the many ruined buildings, there was a barracklike structure on the south side of the hilltop, opposite the long palace. This building, about seventy-eight feet long, was less carefully constructed than the others. There were no wall niches in it, such as those usually found in Inca dwellings.

"This could have been a barracks for Manco's and Titu Cusi's palace guard," he said, "or it might have been built to house the Spanish soldiers who stayed with Manco and murdered him. Notice the flat area, the green between this building and the palace. It might have been the very spot where Manco was killed, when he played at quoits with Perez and Mendez."

When Hiram Bingham returned to Rosaspata with workmen a few days later, in order to dig test excavations, his belief that this was Viticos was further confirmed. The workmen uncovered a great mass of Inca potsherds, Inca whirl bobs, used in spinning cotton and wool thread, as well as Inca shawl pins and other adornments. They also uncovered iron articles: rusted horseshoe nails, buckles, Spanish bridles and saddle ornaments. The Incas had no iron articles of any sort, and so Hiram felt that these objects were European. They had either been taken by the Inca Manco during his raids on the Spanish settlements, or they had been brought here by the Spanish refugees, Perez and Mendez.

Although it entered his mind that these iron articles might have been left much later, by Spanish settlers or modern Peruvians, this did not seem too likely. There were no springs or wells on Rosaspata. Whoever had lived here had had to carry water for miles up a steep and difficult trail. Only the Inca, commanding the labor of thousands of Indians, could afford to live on a waterless mountaintop. It was unlikely that anyone had lived here after the Incas.

One afternoon, one of the diggers uncovered a pair of rusted, Spanish-style scissors. Hiram showed them to Billy Erving. "When the Spanish emissary Rodriguez de Figueroa visited Viticos," he said, "he brought a pair of Spanish scissors as a present for Titu Cusi. I wonder if these were Titu Cusi's scissors. Imagine handling a pair of shears with which the Inca trimmed his nails."

Although Hiram was now sure that he had found Manco's Viticos, he wanted still more proof. "If this is Viticos and the village down below is Puquiura, then the other parts of the puzzle must be nearby. Yurak Rumi and a place called Chuquipalpa should be within walking distance of here."

While spending the nights at the home of an Indian friend of Mogrovejo, Hiram questioned his host. Had he ever heard of Viticos? No. Did he know of any place called Yurak Rumi? No. Had he heard of a place called Chuquipalpa? No. Did he know of any place where a great white rock stood over a spring of dark water?

Yes!

Hiram almost danced with joy when he heard this.

"I saw this white rock many years ago," said the Indian. "It is over in the next valley, called Los Andenes."

110

"Can you describe it? How big was the rock? Where was the spring?"

"I don't remember," replied the man. "It was very long ago."

Early the next morning, the explorers rode to the Valley of Los Andenes. Without the slightest hesitation, Mogrovejo's Indian friend led them to a large white granite boulder which had been flattened on top and had a carved platform on one side. As Hiram circled the rock, his spirits dampened. "There's no spring."

"Yes, there is water," said Mogrovejo. He, his companion, and another villager led the way to a narrow irrigation ditch. "Here it is," said Mogrovejo, who, by now, was expecting a double bonus for every new discovery made by the party.

"Well, this is certainly not it," Hiram said disappointedly. "But we may as well note it on our maps. The white rock is Inca, and a landmark." He asked Mogrovejo's friend what the name of this place was.

The man did not know, but the other Indian said, "Chuquipalpa."

Hiram's interest perked up. "Yurak Rumi must be somewhere near," he said. "The chronicles mention that close by Viticos, in a village called Chuquipalpa, is the House of the Sun, and in it is a white stone over a spring of water."

Although there seemed to be no sign of a village or its ruins in the area, the many stone terraces, or *andenes*, showed that the valley had once supported a large population. As the explorers spread out, each man searching for a glimpse of ruins, they came upon a number of carved boulders similar to the first one.

111

These rocks were considered to be sacred. The Incas selected them and carved them to represent the founders of the tribe. Finding so many of them in this valley convinced Hiram that the area must have once been a religious center of some sort.

"I suggest we follow the irrigation ditch. It might lead to something, perhaps a spring or lake," Harry Foote said.

The naturalist's hunch proved to be a good one. After following the trickling stream through a dense wood, they came to an open place that was surrounded by thickly wooded hills. It was late afternoon, and an eerie silence seemed to hang over the area as the men suddenly stopped and stared. Directly ahead of them was an enormous white granite boulder, partly sheltered by an Inca temple; part of the boulder overhung a small pool of dark water.

"Yurak Rumi," Hiram murmured.

It was indeed Yurak Rumi, but the Indians of this region, who still considered the place sacred, had given it a new name. They called it Nusta Ispanna. Although the temple buildings surrounding the white rock and spring were in complete ruin, there were enough things to show that this had once been an important ceremonial center. The huge rock was covered with interesting carvings; altarlike platforms and seats had been carved into the west side of the rock. There were also a series of broken sundial projections, the Inca *intihuatana,* or place where the sun is tied.

Hiram felt marvelously elated. He had spent two long years digging back into the past, poring over old chronicles and maps, fitting together a picture of the last Incas and their stronghold, Viticos. He had pieced the picture together; now he had found it. There remained but two nagging thoughts in his mind: Where was Vilcabamba the Old, and what was Machu Picchu?

11.

JUNGLE INTERLUDE

For more than a week Hiram Bingham's group remained in the Viticos area, mapping the ruins on Rosaspata Hill, searching the surrounding countryside to make certain there was no other great white rock over a spring, and questioning the natives concerning Vilcabamba the Old.

One day they were guided to a town not far from Pucyura, a town which bore the name Vilcabamba. It was a semideserted settlement built in the Spanish style. There were no Inca ruins in or around it. Obviously, it was not the place that Titu Cusi had called his "principal seat." It was simply a deserted Spanish mining settlement, undoubtedly the Vilcabamba which Baltazar de Ocampo said the Spaniards had founded in 1572.

While visiting in this settlement, Hiram asked the headman, a mestizo named Condoré, to call together the older villagers for the usual session of questions. One picturesque old man, whose features were Inca-like and whose name was Quispi Cusi, said that the Inca Tupac Amaru had once lived on Rosaspata. This he had heard from his grandfather. Although the old man had never heard of such names as Viticos and Vilcabamba the Old, he said there were important Inca ruins near a place called Conseirvidayoc, which was in the hot jungles, a four-day journey down the Pampaconas River.

Hiram was immediately interested. He remembered that when his party had stopped at Don Pedro Duque's plantation a fortnight ago, one of Don Pedro's friends had mentioned Conseirvidayoc, and that it might be Vilcabamba the Old. Furthermore, the name Pampaconas struck a note in his mind. Although there was no Pampaconas on early maps, a village with the name "Bambaconas" was often mentioned in the Spanish chronicles. When the Spanish viceroy had sent Rodriguez de Figueroa to talk with Titu Cusi, Figueroa had met the Inca near a place called Bambaconas, and the Inca had come there from somewhere in the jungles. Titu Cusi had presented Figueroa with two hampers of peanuts, and a macaw. Both the bird and the nuts were tropical products.

"I think we had better check on it, even though it may be a hard journey," Hiram announced.

"You go to Conseirvidayoc?" Sergeant Carrasco asked with alarm.

"There are ruins," replied Hiram.

"Señores, I warn you against it," said the sergeant. "You will remember what Don Pedro Duque said about that place. It is a region inhabited by savages who shoot poisoned arrows. They kill white men on sight. It is not that I fear for myself, but in Cuzco the authorities entrusted your safety in my hands. You travel through this country so blithely, so unaware of its dangers. Remember what Don Pedro told us about that man Saavedra."

Hiram nodded. In fact, he was quite curious about the man called Saavedra. At Don Pedro's plantation the men had talked about Saavedra as being a mysterious, powerful lord, who controlled an estate in the jungle country. They said he had fifty personal servants, as well as an army of wild Indians armed with bows and poison-tipped arrows. They also said he did not like visitors, and no one had returned from that region alive.

"What do you think?" Hiram asked Harry Foote.

"I don't know," replied the naturalist. "Saavedra may not exist. You know how stories get around. I do know, however, there'll be some interesting insects down there."

"How about you, Billy?" Hiram asked Doctor Erving. "Do you have anything in your medical kit for doctoring poisoned-arrow wounds?"

For an hour the explorers discussed the dangers and difficulties of such a journey. Finally, they decided to

116

go. It just would not do to leave an important Inca ruin unchecked. Orders were given to pack the mules. After some discussion the village headman, Condoré, and some of his men agreed to accompany the expedition.

The route they followed led them into one of the wildest unexplored regions of South America. They crossed the headwaters of the Vilcabamba River and entered the Pampaconas country, an uncharted area fifteen hundred miles wide, a bewildering wilderness of deep green valleys and craggy mountains. Although Hiram Bingham had a recent map by the British Geographical Society and Raimondi's chart of the region, neither of them was useful here. He was to learn, two years later, when he led another expedition into this region, that his maps were completely inadequate. His topographer on the second expedition, Alfred H. Bumstead, discovered that the Apurimac and Urubamba Rivers were actually thirty miles farther apart than was shown on any map, and that a great range of mountains and valleys stood between them.

After following the most difficult of trails, the expedition finally arrived at Pampaconas, a miserable village clinging to a mountainside at an elevation of ten thousand feet. Here Hiram found that the headman of the village, a sturdy Indian named Guzman, had once been to Conseirvidayoc. Guzman said he had seen some ruins at a place called Espiritu Pampa. He also said there was a lord named Saavedra who lived there, but this mysterious man might not bother the explorers if they were not rubber gatherers.

Since the trail beyond Pampaconas was so dangerous and uncertain, Hiram decided to leave the mules at

117

Pampaconas and to use Indian pack bearers. This, however, proved difficult because the Indians in the area were very shy and refused to work for foreigners. When Sergeant Carrasco found he could hire no men, delaying the expedition for more than a day, Evaristo Mogrovejo and Condoré rounded up the pack bearers by a simple ruse. The two old men went into the country and whenever they came upon an Indian working his tiny plot of land, they went up to the man and shook his hand. In South America, handshaking is an important social formality. People unfailingly shake hands when they meet and when they part. But when Mogrovejo and Condoré shook hands, they deftly left a silver dollar in the Indian's hand. Having done this, they solemnly and pompously said, "You have accepted official pay for services you must now render."

Even though Indians carried the heaviest camp equipment, the journey now became a nightmare for the three Americans. A steady rain fell; the humidity soared. The jungle was so dense that every foot of the way had to be hacked clear with machetes. Clouds of flies and mosquitoes buzzed constantly around their heads. At the end of each day the travelers were so exhausted they hardly had the energy to clean and maintain their equipment, yet they had to, because the heat and humidity caused all articles to corrode or turn green with mold.

One late afternoon after camp had been made, as Hiram Bingham was trying to straighten out some candles he carried in his pack—they had softened and knotted in the oppressive heat—Harry Foote held his hand out, showing Hiram a fat, hairless grub. "Want supper?" he asked.

118

"I'll eat *cuy* or guinea pigs or spider monkeys, but not that," said Hiram. "What is it?"

"Our pack bearers are out there collecting these," replied Harry. "They bite the heads off, then eat them. Quite a delicacy. Something for our next Yale Club banquet."

On the following day, August 15th, the party was deep in jungle country. Toward noon the guide, Guzman, raised his hand, calling a halt. He told Sergeant Carrasco that one of the Indian pack bearers should be sent ahead to warn the savages that the expedition was a peaceful one. A man was selected for this mission. Although he did not appear to relish the job of going off alone in the jungle, he put down his pack and slipped away into the dense brush. Meanwhile the travelers waited, the nerves of each man alert. The slightest sound —the snap of a twig, the unnerving call of red howler monkeys in the towering trees—seemed to signal an ambush. When would Saavedra send his army of bowmen against them?

Suddenly there came the sound of breaking branches, as though someone were crashing headlong through the jungle. Hiram thought it was their pack bearer being pursued. Sergeant Carrasco and Harry Foote raised their guns. All at once a young Peruvian boy burst out of the thickets. Hiram stared at him in disbelief. The boy was dressed as though he were going to school in Cuzco.

"Don't shoot, gentlemen," the lad cried in Spanish. "Don't shoot. My father, Don Saavedra, sends me to welcome you."

Harry Foote lowered his gun. The sergeant, however, remained alert, for he still suspected an ambush.

119

"No, there is no trick," the boy explained.

When he finally convinced them that there was no danger, that no shower of poisoned arrows would rain on them from the thickets, they gathered up their loads and followed him. Soon they reached a well-cleared trail that led to a bright green field of sugar cane. After a short walk through the shoulder-high cane, they came to a clearing and a large, comfortable-looking hut, where a wiry, pleasant man awaited them.

"I am Saavedra," he said. "You are welcome to my home."

For a moment, Hiram simply stared at the man. Where was the dangerous Saavedra who resented strangers entering his domain? Where was the estate with fifty servants? Where was the army of savage Indians? Was this gentlemanly man, this person with finely chiseled features, who spoke excellent Spanish, was he the lord Saavedra? Then Hiram noticed the shy Indian woman and the four children standing behind the man.

As it turned out, Señor Saavedra was simply an intelligent, hard-working pioneer, who had carved a small sugar plantation for himself out of these wilds so he could send his sons to school in Cuzco. The shy Indian woman was his wife. There was also an Indian girl, whom Hiram later described as "a wild-eyed, maid-of-all-work, evidently the only savage present."

After providing the explorers with a tasty dinner of roast chicken, rice, and sweet manioc, Señor Saavedra told them about the Inca ruins at Espiritu Pampa. "The place is very hard to get into," he explained. "If you will lend me your pack bearers, I'll send my son with them to cut a trail." While the trail was being opened,

Saavedra showed Hiram a number of bronze axes, Inca pottery, and other artifacts he had found on his own property. Although Hiram found these objects very interesting, he could not help but keep worrying about Saavedra's young son and the pack bearers. During lunch he had overheard Saavedra telling Sergeant Carrasco that there were Indians in the forest who used poisoned arrows. But Hiram worried needlessly.

The following day the trail was opened. When the explorers reached Espiritu Pampa, it seemed as if the work and effort were hardly worth while. The ruins, located near an Indian village composed of a few huts, were no more interesting than the village itself. As Hiram peered at the few crumbled stone walls, half-hidden by vines and trees, he doubted that the Inca Titu Cusi had ever bothered to come this far into the jungle.

Just as he was blaming himself for wasting the expedition's valuable time, the jungle brush ahead of him parted, and a half-naked man stepped into view. The man was a muscular, bronzed young Indian who wore a loincloth and carried a strong bow and long arrows. Hiram stood absolutely still. He stared at the Indian, and the Indian stared at him. Then the brush moved again. A second Indian appeared, then a third Indian. The third Indian was cross-eyed.

The first Indian said something in a language that might have been Quichua, but Hiram was not sure. At this moment Saavedra's son appeared. "He is asking if we wish to see other ruins," said the boy.

"How does he know we're looking for ruins?" Hiram asked.

"He has been watching you for days."

121

"What are the ruins called?"

"The Indian says they are called Eromboni, I think—Eromboni Pampa."

"Well, we might as well see them," replied Hiram.

Although he waited until Harry Foote and Sergeant Carrasco joined them before going with the three Indians, Hiram wondered if they were being led into a trap. This impression grew stronger as the Indians led them deeper into a tangle of jungle so thick that nothing could be seen for more than a few feet ahead.

Finally, after more than an hour of crawling under a blanket of vines and cutting through thickets of bamboo, they came to the ruins. Hiram could scarcely believe what he saw. Despite the heavy growth of vines and brush that half hid the ruins, the stone buildings and the artificial terraces and fountains were impressive.

"Good Lord, look at that!" said Harry Foote, pointing to a wall and a doorway where the stonework was as handsomely cut as anything they had seen at Ollantaytambo or on Rosaspata. "I wonder if we've found Vilcabamba the Old!"

Throughout the remainder of that day and the next, Saavedra's energetic young son directed the three Indians and the expedition's pack bearers in the task of clearing away the jungle growth from the more important buildings. As each structure was revealed, allowing Hiram to take measurements and make a map of the site, the surer he was that he had found an important archaeological site. The workmanship and the size of the buildings—the foundation of one was 192 feet long—convinced him that this must be the place where Titu

Cusi sometimes came to escape the biting cold of the highland winters.

Although this place might have been Titu Cusi's jungle retreat, and, very possibly, the place to which the last Inca, Tupac Amaru, was retreating when Captain Garcia and his men captured the fortress on Rosaspata, Hiram was certain it was not Vilcabamba the Old. It had taken their expedition five days to reach this place from Pucyura. The Augustinians, Father Marcos and Father Diego, had said that Vilcabamba the Old was hardly more than two hard days' travel from Puquiura.

Vilcabamba the Old is somewhere else, he thought.

12.

THE MYSTERIES OF MACHU PICCHU

Although Hiram Bingham felt he had not yet solved the mystery of the whereabouts of Vilcabamba the Old, by September the change in seasons forced him to suspend the search. The season of heavy rains was beginning. In a short time it would turn the rivers of the Andes into raging torrents that would be utterly impassable. It was time now to undertake the second objective of the expedition: a survey of the Pacific coast region along the seventy-third meridian, and the measurement of Mount Coropuna.

The three sections of the expedition held a reunion in Cuzco, where they pooled their information and excited the scholars at the University of Cuzco with details of what they had found. Kai Hendriksen and Paul Lanius, who had spent weeks on Machu Picchu, brought in maps and reports which showed that the ruins there were more extensive and more important than Hiram had estimated. This information alone was enough to warrant another, larger expedition to the mountain ridge. But that would have to wait for another dry season.

While the other members of the expedition continued their survey over one of the highest passes in the Andes, then down toward the coast, Hiram and Herman Tucker went to Arequipa to begin the assault of Mount Coropuna, which some geographers said was the highest peak in the Western Hemisphere.

Leaving Arequipa on October 2nd, the small party spent days crossing the great Peruvian desert, finally reaching a fifteen-thousand-foot plateau at the base of Coropuna. In one of the plateau villages they tried to hire guides, but discovered that the people living within sight of the snow-covered mountain feared going near it. They believed it was a place of the gods. They told stories about a warm paradise on top of the mountain, where monkeys, birds, tropical fruit, and flowers could be found.

The last stage of the climb began on October 14th. On that day Hiram, Herman Tucker, and a Peruvian professor named Alejandro Coello climbed to the 17,300-foot level where they established a base camp. The following morning, braving the cold—seven below zero Fahrenheit—and climbing without oxygen equipment, the

125

three men struggled up the icy slopes at a snail's pace. They suffered intense headaches, their pulses ran high, and they had to rest and regain their strength each hundred yards.

Finally, at noon, they reached the broad, flat, snow-covered crest. It was a dramatic moment for the three men. They had scaled what was said to be the highest peak on the continent. Hiram and Tucker unrolled a small American flag and a Yale University banner and planted them on the crest.

After resting for a short while, they unpacked their scientific equipment. As Hiram set up the aneroid to read the elevation of the mountain, he began blinking at the needle. To his surprise and dismay, the needle gave him an elevation of only 21,525 feet above sea level. This was far below the official elevation of Mount Aconcagua—22,763 feet. Tucker now set up the aneroid he had carried with him. It gave a higher reading, 22,500 feet, but it was still not enough.

Although deeply disappointed with the readings, the three climbers took some comfort in the fact that their instruments seemed faulty. Perhaps Mount Coropuna was still the highest. A few weeks later, even this faint hope was dashed when the other sections of the Yale expedition, led by Isaiah Bowman and Kai Hendriksen, were able to make more accurate measurements and found that the peak was only 21,703 feet above sea level.

At the end of the year the expedition returned to the United States. Its work had been highly successful. It had probed the secrets of the Incas, and, in locating the "long palace" at Viticos, it had solved a geographic mystery which had tantalized men for three hundred years. But in solving one mystery, other mysteries had been suggested: What was Machu Picchu? Were there larger ruins on nearby Huayna Picchu? Were these places Vilcabamba, or was Vilcabamba .the Old still hidden, waiting to be discovered? The only way to find the answers was to continue the search.

The administrators at Yale University were so impressed with the results of the expedition—the maps of new regions, the archaeological discoveries, the fine collection of insects and plants brought back by Harry Foote—that a new expedition to Peru was authorized. The university gave ten thousand dollars, and the National Geographic Society matched this sum, in order to send a more completely staffed and equipped group. This was just the beginning.

Hiram Bingham was put in charge of the 1912 Yale–National Geographic Expedition, as well as two larger expeditions that went back to Peru in 1914 and 1915.

The 1912 expedition was split up into groups, as had been done with the first expedition, each group carrying on specialized work. One group mapped the Cuzco Basin, another explored and mapped the Viticos region, another continued the investigation of the Urubamba Valley, while the main group cleared and restored Machu Picchu. Enjoying the full support of the Peruvian government and the Prefecture of Cuzco, the expedition was able to hire enough workmen to reveal the secrets of Machu Picchu.

However, before Hiram could put his men and their equipment to work upon the cloud-shrouded mountain ridge, he realized that some easier road up the mountain must be found. The route he had taken two years earlier was much too dangerous. He assigned the job to Kenneth C. Heald, a husky young mining engineer from Colorado.

Heald, who had climbed almost every difficult peak in the American Rockies, decided to build a trail up the east side of Machu Picchu instead of following the old west path. He began by constructing a rustic, but substantial bridge, farther upstream than the old log bridge. While he poked through the thick brush, surveying a trail up the mountainside, his crew of Quichua workmen followed, clearing and widening the path. The task was no easy one. Heald and his men were confronted by dangers almost every yard of the way.

The mountainside was infested with venomous snakes. During the first week of work, eight poisonous reptiles were killed. Heald himself killed two tropical rattlers, or bushmasters—the largest and most deadly viper in the world.

When the pack trail to Machu Picchu was completed, a larger work-crew, supervised by Dr. George F. Eaton of Yale's Peabody Museum, and by Elwood C. Erdis, a civil engineer, camped among the ruins on the mountain ridge to begin the enormous task of clearing away the blanket of brush and vines smothering most of the buildings. The job was no easy one because the jungle grew with alarming rapidity. Erdis reported that during a four-month period he had a crew of thirty to forty men constantly clearing brush with their machetes. Within a month after they had cleared an area, the bamboo and mesquite was crowding over it again.

The tedious work was worth while. As the mountain-

128

top was cleared, Hiram Bingham could see that the ruins he had discovered were far more extensive than he and his friends on the 1910 expedition had imagined. There was a veritable maze of roofless buildings, little plazas, and so many stone stairways winding in and out that he began calling Machu Picchu "the city of stairways." There were over a hundred large and small sets of stairways, connecting different terraces. In some places the stairs were so narrow that Hiram had to twist his broad shoulders sideways as he climbed them. In other places the steps were wide. In certain places a flight of six to ten steps was carved out of a single massive boulder.

Most of the buildings had well-framed doorways opening upon the stairs or upon the plazas. Very few of the buildings had windows, but these small windows opened out on magnificent vistas of the canyon and mountains. Looking through them, Hiram easily understood why the Quichua name for window meant the holes that see.

Throughout this city-in-the-clouds there were many small garden-terraces where the inhabitants of Machu Picchu probably grew their corn and potatoes. Unlike the Inca fortress, Viticos, on Rosaspata, Machu Picchu had its own water. A perfect system of channels and aqueducts carried water almost a mile, from the mountainside to the fountains in the heart of the city.

As the work of clearing and restoration progressed, it was evident that there were two styles of buildings in Machu Picchu. The more recent buildings seemed to have been constructed at the time of the Spanish conquest of Peru; the finer, more elaborate structures were far older. The most stunning buildings were situated on the west side of the city.

Hiram never grew tired of strolling in this section. He enjoyed crossing the Sacred Plaza, passing in front of the Temple of the Three Windows, then going up a flight of stairs to the top of a small hill, where he could look down upon the roofless city, and beyond it, to the breathtaking canyon and the towering walls of distant snow-capped ranges. Upon this crest was a small temple made of beautifully fitted white stones. A few feet from it was the Inca sundial, or *intihuatana,* carved out of the solid rock and sticking up like a stubby pole.

The *intihuatana* was in perfect condition. To Hiram this was proof that the Spaniards had never visited this isolated retreat. Feeling that the sundials were part of a devilish pagan ceremony, the Spaniards and their priests always knocked off the protruding finger, or nubbin, on the dial.

There was no doubt in Hiram's mind that Machu Picchu was a kind of fortress. Its very position on the ridge and crest of a high mountain made it secure. The canyon and river, surrounding it on three sides, were like a gigantic moat around a medieval castle. As if this had not made it secure enough, the ancient builders had surrounded the city with carefully constructed walls, so high that no man could scale them. There was but one gateway into the city, and, although no sign of a gate had been found, Hiram believed that there had once been one, made of heavy logs.

While gazing out over the deserted city, where vivid dahlias, begonias, and enormous yellow lilies grew among the ruins, Hiram wondered what its secrets were.

130

It was the largest city in this province, larger than Ollantaytambo and Viticos. It was a city suspended in the sky above the most inaccessible corner of the most inaccessible region of the Central Andes. Who had built it? Who had lived here?

As careful excavations were done among the ruins, further mysteries were posed. Although numerous potsherds were found in the excavations, as well as a few small bronze artifacts, there was not a single piece of whole pottery, or artifacts of any importance. It was as if Machu Picchu had been abandoned suddenly, its inhabitants carrying away with them all their valued possessions.

"If there were graves, we might find something in them," Dr. Eaton pointed out. "Thus far we've found neither burial places, nor anything in and around the buildings."

When Hiram asked the Indian workmen if they had seen any graves, there was no answer. Even Richarte and Alvarez, the two Indians who had made their home on Machu Picchu for so long, and who knew the area perfectly, remained silent.

"There must be caves nearby or in the canyon," said Hiram.

"No caves, none anywhere," replied Richarte.

Something in the man's tone of voice gave Hiram the impression that the workmen were silent because they were afraid that disturbing the bones of the ancient people might bring bad luck. Remembering how effective rewards had been on the previous expedition, he offered a Peruvian sol for every cave with bones in it that a workman might find. The offer worked like a charm.

131

The next day Richarte and Alvarez found eight caves. Soon, more than fifty caves were located.

Dr. Eaton, who was a specialist in osteological studies —the study of bones—began a careful investigation of the numerous skeletons found in the caves. At the same time, Hiram and his assistant began cataloguing and photographing the artifacts found in these burial caves.

In one cave, which Dr. Eaton decided must have been the grave of an Inca high priestess, the Mama-cuna who supervised the convent of the Virgins of the Sun, the skeleton of the priestess was found in its mummy wrappings. Along with it there were numerous treasures: several large bronze shawl pins, bronze tweezers, sewing needles made of maguey spines, a dainty bronze curette with an ornamental head of a flying bird, a fine cooking pot, a beaker decorated with a snake in bas-relief, and a distinctive, bronze, concave mirror.

One day, after he was well along in his investigation, Dr. Eaton called Hiram to his tent. He tapped a sheaf of papers he had been working over and said, "A most remarkable thing, Hiram. Look at this! In all the caves in the area we're calling Cemetery 1, we've found fifty skeletons. All but four of them are of females. Furthermore, of the total 173 skeletons found in all the caves, I have determined, with fair certainty, that 150 are female."

"This is most interesting," said Hiram.

"Oddly, the male skeletons that we have found are almost all of delicate men," said Eaton. "The bone structure is definitely not of husky men, such as workmen or warriors."

"What do you make of this?"

"I don't like to guess," said the scholar, "but from the artifacts we found in the caves, and from the sex of the skeletal remains, it seems reasonable to suggest that these were rather special burials, especially those in Cemetery 1, which is closest to the city. I would conclude that the skeletons are of the Chosen Women, or Virgins of the Sun. The male skeletons may be those of priests."

"I wonder," said Hiram, "could it have been that the last occupants of Machu Picchu were women? That there were no men left?"

His thoughts turned to the Spanish chronicles which he had searched through so often. He recalled the story of Father Marcos and Father Diego and their interest in Vilcabamba the Old, where they believed there was a "University of Idolatry." Somewhere near that Vilcabamba, the two priests suffered the ordeal of temptation, when a large number of Chosen Women were sent by Titu Cusi's priests to make the two men forget their religious vows of chastity. Were they the same Chosen Women from the nunnery high on Machu Picchu, the same women whose skeletons had been found in the burial caves?

When Captain Garcia overran Viticos and finally captured the last Inca, Tupac Amaru, the reports of these events said nothing about a large number of Chosen Women being captured. This, Hiram thought, would indicate that there may not have been any, or perhaps only a few Chosen Women at Viticos and at Yurak Rumi. It seemed to say that most of these Virgins of the Sun might have been here at Machu Picchu. It also gave sup-

133

port to the idea that Machu Picchu might have been the most important Inca ceremonial center in the region, perhaps the religious center—the "University of Idolatry."

Between 1912 and 1915, as the expeditions he led in Peru thoroughly explored the Central Andes, and failed to find any Inca ruins as important and as imposing as those on Machu Picchu, Hiram Bingham was more and more convinced that the mysterious Vilcabamba the Old must be Machu Picchu.

During this time other pieces of the puzzle were found, and fitted into place. While rereading the Inca history written by the seventeenth-century lawyer Fernando Montesinos, Hiram again came upon the story of the ancient Peruvian king named Pachacuti, who was killed when barbarians overran his region. His followers took Pachacuti's body to a place of refuge called Tampu-tocco.

Hiram found that the word *tampu*, in Quichua, meant inn, hill, or cave; *tocco* meant a niche or window. Together the two words could mean a place of temporary abode.

In Montesinos' history several Peruvian kings lived at Tampu-tocco. "The faithful vassals were happy in Tampu-tocco, for there, according to the legends of the Amautas, is a very celebrated cave where the Incas had their origin, and they affirmed as a certainty that there have never been seen there earthquakes, pestilence nor earth tremors. . . ." Montesinos also wrote that Manco Capac, the first ruler to be called Inca, established his court in Tampu-tocco.

Hiram Bingham also found in the work of the Inca

historian Pachacuti Yamqui Salcamayhua and account describing how Manco Capac founded Cuzco and enlarged his domain, then, "afterward he ordered works to be executed at the place of his birth, consisting of a masonry wall with three windows, which were the emblems of the house of his father whence he descended. The windows were named for his paternal and maternal grandparents and his uncles."

To Hiram the three windows in the sacred building on Machu Picchu seemed to fit this account perfectly. Although Montesinos seemed to think Tampu-tocco was about twenty miles from Cuzco, at a place called Paccari Tampu, Hiram decided the historian was wrong. He made a journey to Paccari Tampu, where he located the ruins of a small Inca village, as well as some caves. He found no buildings with windows, especially three windows, to justify the name Tampu-tocco. Furthermore, he reasoned, Paccari Tampu was too close to Cuzco to be the safe refuge to which the followers of King Pachacuti had fled. Also, being close to Cuzco, it was subject to the same terrible earthquakes which often shook that city. Machu Picchu, on the other hand, showed no signs of earthquake damage.

While digging into other colonial records, Hiram found further references to Tampu-tocco and Manco Capac. On January 21, 1572, the Spanish viceroy Francisco de Toledo, while trying to track down anyone who might become a successor to the last Inca, held a court of inquiry at which fifteen Indian leaders were questioned about the history of the Incas. They said that the first Inca, Manco Capac, came from Tampu-tocco. They denied knowing where this was.

135

Hiram wondered whether these men did not know the location of Tampu-tocco, or whether they were keeping the secret of its location from the Spaniards because it was so sacred a place. He suspected the latter. Why had Manco II and Titu Cusi let Spaniards visit at Viticos, and at the same time kept them from visiting Vilcabamba the Old? Was Vilcabamba the Old so sacred a place?

Although he felt he might never positively prove that the original name of Machu Picchu was Tampu-tocco, Hiram was sure that the place was held in special regard by the Incas. It was a place foreigners should be kept away from at all cost.

While rereading Montesinos' history, he also found a clue which made him think that young Manco II, after fleeing to the mountains from the Spaniards attacking him at Ollantaytambo, had gone to Machu Picchu rather than to Viticos. In his history Montesinos described how Pizarro had captured Manco's favorite wife, and how the conquistador had tortured her and put her to death. As the woman was dying, she begged her attendants to place her body "in a basket and float it down the Urubamba River, that the current might take it to her husband, the Inca."

Perhaps Manco and his wife shared the secret of Machu Picchu. Perhaps she knew where he was going—the sacred, impregnable city on the mountain ridge above the swift torrents of the Urubamba River. It seemed very likely that Manco had fled to this retreat to recuperate, to pay his respects to his ancestors and the Sun, and to gather supporters around him before moving to Viticos to direct his attacks upon the Spaniards.

Though he was growing more certain that Machu Picchu was indeed Vilcabamba the Old, Hiram was puzzled as to how it was given this name. Scholars in Lima and at the University of Cuzco were able to help him now. They told him that the old Inca name for the Urubamba River had been Uilca-mayu. Since it was the most important river in the entire region, its name had also been given to the entire province.

They also explained that Uilca (also spelled Huilca) was the name of a subtropical tree, noted for its medicinal properties. Powder ground from the seeds of the tree was used by the ancient Inca as a kind of magic snuff. The Inca priests inhaled the narcotic powder, drawing it into the nose with a pair of tubes. When they had sniffed enough of it, the drug put them in a hypnotic state that was accompanied by colorful visions.

"Thus you see," explained one of the Cuzco scholars, "Uilca-pampa or Huilca-pampa, when the Spaniards pronounced it, became Vilcabamba. In Quichua, it means place where the Uilca tree grows."

One of the university men added that according to Montesinos' history, Huilcanota, the fifty-third king of Peru, may have been the discoverer of the vision-producing plant, and thus received his name.

While Hiram Bingham was assembling these various pieces of the puzzle, Dr. O. F. Cook, one of the naturalists on the 1915 expedition, made an unusual discovery. Near one of the new bridges along the government road, on a small flat, or pampa, not far from Machu Picchu, he found a *huilca* tree. This was another small but important part in the puzzle, because it indicated to Hiram that the sacred tree was native to the area around Machu Picchu. Perhaps the Inca priests had even cultivated it upon one of the terraces among the temples. The Inca priests certainly used the drug in their ceremonies, because one of the double tubes for sniffing it was found in the diggings at the ruins.

Although all the signs seemed to say that Machu Picchu was Vilcabamba the Old, one very important part of the puzzle was still missing. According to Father Marcos and Father Diego, Vilcabamba was two or three days' hard journey from Viticos and Puquiura. On the numerous trips that Hiram and other members of the various expeditions had made between Machu Picchu and Puquiura, even when they pushed themselves, it had always taken five to seven days' travel. Furthermore, these journeys were made on muleback, along the new government road; the Augustinian friars had been on foot.

During the 1911 expedition, Harry Foote had suggested that the Incas might have had a short cut between Puquiura (Pucyura) and Vilcabamba the Old. Until 1915 no such short cut was found. Hiram's skilled geographers and mapmakers crisscrossed the province. They discovered and mapped a large number of old Inca roads linking various ruins, including the many fortified outposts which encircled Machu Picchu. No one found a short route.

It was not until late in the season of 1915 that one member of the party heard a rumor about such a short cut. It was a road which the Indians had once used in going from Pucyura to the Huadquiña plantation, just a few miles from Machu Picchu. To check out the rumor, Hiram and a small party crossed the rugged region from the pass between snow-capped Mount Soray and Mount Salcantay to Pucyura. They found no sign of the road. However, while they were visiting at the house of an old friend, Andreas Quintanilla, in Pucyura, an old man in the village told them that he knew of a road to Huadquiña which no one used any longer.

"Can you lead us along the road?" Hiram asked.

"*Pues*, Señor," said the old man, "perhaps I can find it, and perhaps not, but who knows."

The old man was better than his word. Setting out from Pucyura in the direction of Choqquequirau, he turned to the east, picking up the faint trace of an Inca paved road. At times the road vanished, obliterated by landslides, and the party had to spend exasperating hours trying to pick up the trail. Sometimes the ruins of Inca resthouses were the only signs that they were on the road. Soon the party entered a wild region dotted with lakes and bogs. Had it not been the dry season, this bleak area would have been impassable. It was the kind of terrain that could easily be flooded. It reminded Hiram Bingham of Father Marcos' story—the two priests, their monastic robes tucked up around their waists, wading through icy water, while the joke-loving Titu Cusi rode on a palanquin carried by his servants.

As the exploring party passed a dark green lake, a body of water larger than any they had seen thus far, Hiram called ahead to the guide, "What is the name of the lake?"

"Ungacacha," the guide shouted.

139

A sudden thrill ran through Hiram. Ungacacha! It was the name Friar Marcos had given to the place where he and Father Diego had waded through the icy water.

A little later Hiram discovered that he had misunderstood the guide. The man had said Yanaccocha, Black Lake. However, in Quichua, the sound of the two words, though spelled differently, was almost the same. It was quite possible, Hiram decided, that Father Marcos, writing about his adventure sometime afterward, had made the same mistake.

Shortly after passing through the Lake Yanaccocha area, the Inca road led to the ruins of an Inca storehouse at Yuracrumiyoc, which Hiram had visited in 1911. The discovery delighted him. A good road linked the ruins with the plantation at Huadquiña. The last part of the puzzle had fallen into place. Deducting the hours lost in tracing the obliterated parts of the road, the entire journey from Pucyura to Machu Picchu had taken less than three days.

13.

EXPLORER INTO FLYER

While Hiram Bingham was in Peru fitting together the last parts of the puzzle which identified Machu Picchu as Vilcabamba the Old, World War I had started in Europe.

When Hiram returned to the United States after the 1915 expedition, he saw signs that his own country was being drawn inevitably into the war. Never a person to sit back and do nothing while exciting events occurred around him, Hiram quickly wrote up his reports on the Yale University—National Geographic Society Expeditions to Peru; then he began looking for some way of helping his country in the growing emergency.

In 1917 Hiram was forty-two years old. He had a reputation as a history professor and as an explorer. He also had a rapidly growing family. With such a background and responsibilities he might easily have sat out the war. But to remain inactive was not his cup of tea.

Reading about the part aviation was beginning to play over the grim battlefields of Europe, intrigued his lively imagination. Certain that his own country would soon be in the war, he began asking questions about American aviation. Some of the answers he received shocked him. He discovered that the army and navy had practically no air force. The generals and admirals were too preoccupied with ships, tanks, and ground forces to bother about a nonsensical thing like flying. On the eve of war, there were no more than twenty-five competent flying instructors in the entire country.

Convinced that the United States should develop a strong air force, Hiram decided to do something about it. He soon made friends with one of the nation's pioneer flyers, Glenn Curtiss, and in March 1917 he enrolled at the Curtiss Flying School in Florida, where future army pilots were learning the rudiments of flying. By now Hiram's hair was turning gray, and he was looked upon as the old man of the school by most of the younger officers, who had been born when he was a college undergraduate.

Learning to fly during those years was a haphazard and dangerous undertaking. Weather reports received at the flying field were sketchy. No one knew whether the training planes, held together with wire and glue, and

142

operated by a poor quality gasoline, would get off the ground or not. The plane that Hiram was assigned to take up for his first solo flight had turned over twice during the previous twenty-four hours, either at take-off or in landing. His own flight in it was quite short; he had hardly gotten into the air before he had to make an emergency landing because the engine carburetor choked on dirty gasoline. Nevertheless, within a few months he had mastered the ungainly F-type flying boat and the more versatile army Jennie, or JN-4.

Before the year ran out, he had won his wings and spurs. The spurs irritated him. Although he had been born in Hawaii, he was a down-to-earth New Englander who felt that the army's policy of dressing flying officers like cavalry officers was quite silly. As long as he was in the army, he fought against the official regulation requiring flying men to wear cavalry spurs.

Shortly after the United States entered the war, Hiram was transferred to the War Department offices in Washington, D.C., to help plan an army training program for pilots and ground-crew technicians. His university background and connections proved most useful. His own training as a pilot made him realize that the best manpower pool for flyers was the campus. College athletics gave young men quick and sure reflexes; their academic studies made it easier for them to learn the complexities of air navigation, flying, and military strategy. Before long, Hiram was traveling back and forth across the country, visiting colleges and setting up air training programs on campus after campus.

Having done all he could to help build a training program at home, Hiram went to France in 1918 to take over the command of the largest American military training school in Europe, the Third Aviation Instruction Center at Issoudun. There, between occasional flying sorties over the German lines, he helped shape American air power at a time when few people realized how important it would become. Finally, on March 8, 1919, just two years after he had learned to fly, he was honorably discharged with the rank of lieutenant colonel.

Although he returned to his post at Yale, he was drawn to the challenge and excitement of public affairs. Thus, in 1922, he began what would be a long, distinguished, and sometimes stormy career in politics. That year he was elected lieutenant governor of the State of Connecticut. Two years later he won the governorship. However, before he was installed in office, one of the state's senators committed suicide; Hiram ran for this post in the special election, and won it. For a period of a few hours he was the only man in United States history to hold simultaneously the offices of lieutenant governor and governor of a state, as well as the U.S. senatorship.

He served in the Senate during the administrations of Presidents Coolidge and Hoover. Then, in 1951, even though he was a Republican, he served as chief of President Truman's Loyalty Review Board. During these years in politics, he found time to make one more trip to Machu Picchu.

In October of 1948 he returned to Peru as the honored guest of President Bustamante. Hiram was seventy-two years old. His hair was a snowy thatch, yet he had a youthful spring in his step. Arriving in Cuzco, he was greeted by the mayor of the city, the prefect of the province, the archbishop, several Peruvian senators and the

144

American ambassador to Peru. Unfortunately Hiram's host, President Bustamante, was unable to be present; a revolution in Lima, a few days before, had forced him to flee.

The president's absence, however, did not dampen the celebrations. The reason for Hiram's visit was the dedication of a new road called the Hiram Bingham Highway. Although the road was no superhighway, it was a superb engineering job. It twisted and turned up the sheer side of Machu Picchu, following the same trail Hiram had crawled up when he had first discovered the marvelous ridgetop Inca ruins.

After being showered with flowery speeches, Hiram led the official party up the stone stairway to the granite observatory where Inca priests had once tied the sun to a stone nubbin, marking the seasonal solstice. As they looked down upon the "city of stairways," upon the Temple of the Three Windows, upon the Inca's Palace and the House of the Chosen Women, Hiram retold the story of Machu Picchu.

He spoke quietly of Manco's struggle against the Spanish invaders, of how Manco and his sons had made this fortress in the sky, towering above the torrents of the Urubamba River, the last home for the Virgins of the Sun. He explained how the Inca men had abandoned even this last refuge, leaving the Chosen Women to live on alone, one dying after the other, keeping the secret of this beautiful mountaintop.

14.

FIFTY YEARS OF DISCOVERIES

On June 6, 1956, Hiram Bingham died at the age of eighty in Washington, D.C.

In the forty years between his last Yale University–National Geographic Society Expedition to Peru and his death, far more information was uncovered about the ancient Peruvian civilizations than was gathered during the previous four hundred years. The teamwork of trained men and the development of new scientific techniques has given us a picture of Peru's history which, though still incomplete, is quite different from what was

146

available to Hiram Bingham when he set out in search of the Inca's Viticos and Vilcabamba the Old.

Archaeology and anthropology had to wait until after World War I to really flower. After the war these sciences began to develop many new methods of investigation. For example, the ways of classifying and studying the sequences of pottery made by ancient man were improved. Archaeologists found better ways to determine the age and the order in which pottery was made, as well as how widely it was distributed. Pottery, like man, leaves its own distinctive fingerprints.

Today the explorer-archaeologist seldom works alone. He often calls upon the botanist, the geologist, the metallurgist, the medical researcher, the agronomist, the physicist, the linguistics expert, and even the astronomer to help him unveil the mysteries of the past. He may stand by while a petroleum engineer has drillers bring up a coring from deep in the earth, which contains the seeds ancient man once planted. He anxiously waits while the botanist identifies the seeds as a primitive corn. Then the seeds are sent to the physicist's laboratory where, by means of Carbon 14 dating and measurements, the age of the seeds is determined. All this scientific work is done to prove that the corn planted by ancient man was not domesticated from a wild corn. Ancient man developed it by crossbreeding several seed plants that he was already using.

When Hiram Bingham began exploring in Peru, these methods of investigation were in their infancy. For his ideas about the history of the Peruvian Indians, he had to rely on pottery and ruins which no one could date with any certainty, and on the Spanish colonial chronicles written by men who only knew about the Incas. He suspected that the Indian cultures went back many many centuries, but he had no idea how many centuries, or how many stages of civilization there might have been.

Since the 1920s, however, we have made great strides toward filling in Peru's pre-Hispanic history. We know now that there were various levels of civilization and highly cultured societies long before the Incas. There was actually a kind of Pan-Peruvian Indian culture covering an enormous region, in which, from several hundred years before the time of Christ to the time of the Spanish conquest, neighboring civilizations developed. Sometimes they were in contact with one another, sometimes they were not.

Neither Hiram Bingham nor other Peruvian scholars at the turn of the century had any clear idea how old the Inca culture was, or exactly where it fitted into the whole picture. Hiram believed that the Incas were descendants of an ancient line of Peruvian kings. Today it has been fairly well determined that the Incas were newcomers. Like the Aztecs of Mexico, they were the inheritors of earlier cultures. They took over the techniques, the skills, and the arts that had already been highly developed in Peru. Even the so-called Inca roads had already been developed before the Incas attained power.

The Incas first came on the Peruvian scene somewhere around A.D. 1300. They were then merely a small *ayllu*, that is, a kin-group or large cluster of families joined in a kind of tribe. During the first two hundred years of their settling in the Cuzco region, the Incas were occupied in minor warfare with small neighboring tribes. It was not until about 1438, under Pachacuti, the ninth Inca, that their history of great conquest and real expansion began. In actuality the life of their empire covered a period of about a hundred years.

From his readings of the Inca and Spanish chronicles, Hiram Bingham believed that Manco Capac was the founder of the Inca dynasty, and that he had left Tamputocco (Machu Picchu) to lead his people to Cuzco. Scholars, today, are very doubtful about this. They feel that Manco Capac may simply be a name representing a composite of early chiefs, or a kind of folk-hero. According to the Peruvian expert John H. Rowe, the Inca rulers are as follows:

1. Manco Capac	?	
2. Sinchi Roca	?	
3. Lloqui Yupanqui	13th century	
4. Mayata Capac	"	"
5. Capac Yupanqui	"	"
6. Inca Roca	14th century	
7. Yuhuar Huaca	"	"
8. Viracocha Inca	"	"
9. Pachacuti Inca Yupanqui	1438–1471	
10. Topu Inca Yupanqui	1471–1493	
11. Huayna Capac	1493–1525	
12. Huascar and Atahualpa	1525–1532	

The Incas at Viticos

1. Manco II	1534–1545
2. Sayri Tupac	1545–1560
3. Titu Cusi	1560–1570
4. Tupac Amaru	1570–1571

149

Recent discoveries and developments in Peruvian archaeology seem to indicate that Hiram Bingham's estimates concerning the age of Machu Picchu and its origin were wrong, and that many of his ideas about ancient Peruvian history were also in error. Nevertheless, it is not really important that he linked the Incas too closely with earlier Indian civilizations. Whether his ideas concerning the age of Machu Picchu were wrong or right, Hiram Bingham was correct, at least, in believing the mountaintop citadel was the last place where the Incas worshiped the sun, the moon, the thunder, and the stars.

Today you can reach Machu Picchu without any great effort. Each year some thirty thousand visitors fly to Cuzco, then ride on the self-propelled railway car to the foot of the sacred mountain. You drive up the Hiram Bingham Highway in station wagons to the mountaintop sanctuary. Soon you will be able to get there with less trouble on a new cable car, and you will be able to spend the night in a new ninety-room hotel overlooking the grandeur of the Urubamba River Canyon.

While you linger among the ruins, you will be haunted by the thought that this is the place where the Chosen Women, the Virgins of the Sun, were left behind when the last Inca fled from the Spaniards. It is the cloud-shrouded sanctuary where the Chosen Women died, one by one, leaving no one to explain the significance of the magnificent ruins.

Although you come to Machu Picchu because it has become a tourist showplace, you will go away realizing that it is also a monument, a memorial to the grandeur of an ancient Indian culture. It is also a reminder that there are men who dream of finding something beyond the ranges, and who go out and find it.

BIBLIOGRAPHY

Bingham, Hiram. *Inca Land*. Boston: Houghton Mifflin Co., 1922.

————. *Lost City of the Incas*. New York: Duell, Sloan & Pearce, 1948.

————. *Machu Picchu, a Citadel of the Incas*. New Haven: Yale University Press, 1930.

————. *Viticos, the Last Inca Capital*. Worcester, Mass.: American Antiquarian Society, 1912.

Bennett, Wendell C., and Bird, Junius B. *Andean Culture History*. Garden City, N.Y.: American Museum Science Books. 1964.

De la Vega, Garcilaso. *Royal Commentaries of the Inca*. Translated by Alain Gheerbrant. New York: Orion Press, 1961.

Means, Philip A. *Fall of the Inca Empire and the Spanish Rule in Peru*. New York: Gordian, 1932.

Prescott, William H. *The Conquest of Peru*. New York: Modern Library.

GLOSSARY

The Incas:

Amautas—Legendary Peruvian kings.

Atahualpa—Last of the pre-Spanish conquest Inca rulers. He and his brother, Huascar, feuded over control of the throne. He was executed by Pizarro. (1525–1532)

Huascar—See above note.

Iluilcanota—Legendary 53rd Amauta king.

Huayna Capac—Inca ruler from 1493 to 1525.

Manco Capac—Legendary founder of the Inca dynasty.

Manco II—Grandson of Huayna Capac. He was made puppet ruler of the Incas by Pizarro. He revolted against the Spanish and set up his own headquarters at Viticos. Murdered in 1545.

Pachacuti—Legendary 64th Amauta king.

Pachacuti Inca Yupanqui—9th Inca ruler (1438–1471).

Pachacuti Yamqui Salcamayhua—A grandson of the Incas and noted historian of the Incas. His work was published in 1620.

Sayri Tupac—Manco II's eldest son. He became the second Inca ruler at Viticos.

Titu Cusi—Manco II's favorite, but illegitimate son. He became the 3rd ruler at Viticos. Died, 1571.

Tupac Amaru—Manco II's youngest son. He succeeded Titu Cusi. He was captured by the Spaniards and executed in 1572.

The Spanish Conquerors, Historians, and Geographers:

Almagro, Diego de—Pizarro's partner in the conquest of Peru. He later fought against Pizarro and was murdered.

Baltazar de Ocampo, Capt.—Spanish soldier, gold prospector; he visited in Viticos shortly after Titu Cusi's death. He wrote a report called "Description of the Province of St. Francis of Victory of Vilcapampa."

Calancha, Fr. Antonio de la—Augustinian friar and historian. Son of a Spanish captain and Peruvian mother. His writings were most important in helping Hiram Bingham locate Viticos. (1584–1654)

Cieza de León, Pedro—Spanish historian, shortly after the conquest of Peru. He wrote "Crómica del Peru." Died in Peru, 1560.

De Soto, Hernando—Spanish conquistador. Took part in the conquest of Peru; later, explored Florida.

Garcia, Capt.—Spanish officer under Gonzalo Pizarro. He pursued and captured the last Inca, Tupac Amaru.

Garcia, Fr. Marcos—Augustinian missionary who lived near Viticos during the reign of Titu Cusi.

Garcilaso Inca de la Vega—Peruvian historian, an Inca of royal blood, born in Cuzco in 1539. Wrote the "Royal Commentaries." Died in Spain.

Mendez, Diego—Spanish soldier who lived at Viticos during the time of Manco II. He was one of the group that killed Manco.

Montesinos, Fernando de—Spanish chronicler of the conquest. He went to Peru as secretary to the viceroy in 1629. Wrote "Memorias Antiguas Historiales del Peru."

154

Ortiz, Fr. Diego—Augustinian friar who also lived near Viticos during the time of Titu Cusi.

Pando, Martín—The mestizo secretary to Titu Cusi.

Perez, Gomez—Spanish soldier who lived at Viticos during the time of Manco II. He was involved in Manco's death.

Pizarro, Francisco—The conqueror of Peru in 1532. See Almagro.

Pizarro, Hernando—Francisco's brother.

Pizarro, Gonzalo—Another brother. He took over control of Peru after Francisco's death.

Raimondi, Antonio—Italian born Peruvian; mapmaker and explorer. He explored the Vilcabamba region in 1868.

Soldan, Paz—Peruvian geographer.

Rodriguez de Figueroa, Diego—Spanish officer and chronicler who visited with Titu Cusi at Viticos.

Toledo, Don Francisco de—Spanish viceroy who conducted the final campaign against the Incas at Viticos.

Places and Things:

Accla—Chosen Women or Virgins of the Sun.

Accla Huaci—House of the Chosen Women (convent).

Choqquequirau—Inca ruins on heights above the Apurimac River. Once believed to have been the secret capital of Manco II.

Chuquipalpa—Village near Yurak Rumi, mentioned in the Spanish chronicles.

Cuzco—The great Andean capital of the Incas at the time of the Conquest.

Eromboni Pampa—Inca ruins in the tropical jungles. The winter retreat of Titu Cusi.

Huayna Picchu—Mountain peak near Machu Picchu.

Huarancalla—(Guarancalla) location of Fr. Diego's mission near Viticos.

Intihuatana—Stone shaft or sun dial, important in Inca sun worship. It means place where the sun is tied.

Machu Picchu—Mountain shoulder overlooking the Urubamba River. On it Bingham found the fabulous ruins which now bear this name. It may have been the Vilcabamba El Viejo of the Spanish chronicles as well as the legendary Tamputocco.

Nusta Ispanna—The present-day name for the Inca shrine, Yurak Rumi.

Ollantaytambo—Winter residence of the Incas in the upper Urubamba Valley.

Pampacona—A valley, river, and village. The village may have been the Bambacona of the Spanish chronicles.

Pucyura—The present-day name of Puquiura, a village near Viticos.

Rosaspata—A hill near Pucyura upon which Manco built his headquarters, Viticos.

Tampu-tocco—Legendary home of Manco Capac. See, Machu Picchu.

Ungacacha—Important place name mentioned in the old chronicles; a key to the location of the lost route between Viticos and Vilcabamba el Viejo.

Urubamba River—The river that passes below Machu Picchu.

Vilcabamba el Viejo (Vilcabamba the Old)—The sacred citadel, or "lost city" of Manco II and Titu Cusi. See Machu Picchu.

Viticos (Uticos & Biticos)—The military headquarters and capital of the last four Incas, who held out against the Spaniards. It is located at the head of the Vilcabamba River, near Pucyura, on Rosaspata.

Yurak Rumi—An Inca religious center not far from Viticos. It was an important landmark because of its spring with a white rock overhanging it.

INDEX

157

158